CHROMATOGRAPHY

AND

ELECTROPHORESIS
ON PAPER

A TEACHING LEVEL MANUAL

by

J. G. Feinberg, B.Sc., M.Sc., D.V.M., M.I.Biol.

and

Ivor Smith, B.Sc., Ph.D., F.R.I.C., M.I.Biol.

for use with the UNIKIT apparatus

LONDON, N.W. 10

© 1962

J. G. FEINBERG AND IVOR SMITH

PUBLISHED BY
SHANDON SCIENTIFIC COMPANY LTD
65 POUND LANE, WILLESDEN, LONDON, N.W.10
AND PRINTED IN GREAT BRITAIN

PREFACE

ONE of the significant aspects of the unprecedented rate of technological progress which we are now experiencing has been the development of new analytical methods and their rapid acceptance and application throughout the world. This has created entirely new problems—particularly in the practical instruction of students and laboratory workers at all levels.

We have felt for some time that there exists a gap between the large number of excellent textbooks and the aids available to the teacher to impart to the student the down-to-earth know-how required for the understanding and practical application of the many new laboratory techniques. To fill this gap we decided to make a beginning by tackling two of the fields with which we are closely connected—namely Chromatography and Electrophoresis. This teaching level manual with its set of specially-developed apparatus is the result, and we sincerely hope that it will be accepted for what it is intended to be: an aid to the busy teacher in planning his course and to the student in acquiring knowledge through practical experiments.

Our warm thanks are due to the authors, Drs. Feinberg and Smith, who have, with great patience, accepted the many suggestions which have been put before them. The publication of the manual would not have been possible without drawing on the many years of experience Dr. Ivor Smith has had in teaching chromatographic and electrophoretic techniques and without his valuable suggestions for the design of the Unikit apparatus and the experiments. We would also like to acknowledge the assistance rendered by Mrs. Margaret Smith in the practical laboratory work she has performed in trying out the experiments and the useful suggestions she has made for their improvement.

October, 1962.   E. R. SHANDON

SHANDON SCIENTIFIC COMPANY LTD.,
65 Pound Lane,
London, N.W.10.

CONTENTS

v

CONTENTS

vi

LIST OF COLOURED PLATES

Facing page

LIST OF NUMBERED ILLUSTRATIONS

As Unikit components are identified by *lettered* Parts, they are not listed below. The page numbers on which they are illustrated will be found under ' UNIKIT ' in the Index at the back of the book.

INTRODUCTION

The enormous advances in scientific knowledge which have been made in the last fifteen years have largely been achieved through the introduction of new scientific techniques. *Paper chromatography* and *paper electrophoresis* are two major factors in the extension of chemical and biological analysis into hitherto difficult or impossible areas.

Teaching of the principles and practice of these two modern techniques is mandatory in every balanced school and college science curriculum. Formerly, the science teacher has had to rely almost entirely on improvisation, or the use of expensive apparatus designed primarily for the technical or advanced research laboratory. There has been a real need for an integrated apparatus and text designed particularly for *teaching-level* paper chromatography and paper electrophoresis.

The Shandon UNIKIT fulfils this need. It does so in one simple, inexpensive apparatus, whose keynote is flexibility. Through ingenuity of design and construction, the UNIKIT is adaptable to an entire range of teaching-level experiments, selected and graded to illustrate the basic principles and methods of paper chromatography and paper electrophoresis.

Three considerations have served as guides in the design of the experiments. First, the substances to be examined and separated will be sufficiently familiar to the students to engage their interest. Second, none of the basic experiments will require longer than 2–3 hours, so that each can be conveniently fitted into the usual laboratory period. The longer, supplementary experiments can either be begun by the instructor beforehand, the students being allowed to finish them and to observe the results, or they can be given to more advanced students to carry out the whole experiment. Both basic and supplementary experiments are included in the manual, so that the UNIKIT may be used at various levels of teaching paper chromatography and paper electrophoresis. The range of the experiments is such as to meet the needs of courses in both chemistry and biology.

Finally, the substances for study have been chosen largely on the basis of their suitability for both chromatographic and electrophoretic experiments. This enables the students to compare the separations obtained by the two different techniques and to observe the different principles in operation.

The UNIKIT, therefore, incorporates everything required for the teaching-level introduction to paper chromatography and paper electrophoresis, apart from commonly-available bulk solvents and chemicals. Used in conjunction with the present manual it will give the science student a firm grounding in these two techniques, which have become an indispensable part of modern chemistry and biology.

SECTION I

PAPER CHROMATOGRAPHY

A Brief History of Paper Chromatography

The early stirrings of paper chromatography are found amongst the ancients. Pliny described a method for detecting iron, which was essentially paper chromatography. But it was not until the early 19th century that a technique was employed with some understanding of the phenomena involved.

It was at that time that the German chemist, Runge, described in his book, *Zur Farbenchemie*, the investigation of many inorganic mixtures by paper chromatography. In 1855, another book of his, *Der Bildungstrieb der Stoffe*, appeared, which was illustrated by insertions of actual paper chromatograms carried out by his assistants.

Following in Runge's steps, came Schönbein and his pupil, Goeppelsroeder, who formed a team for the early investigation of capillary analysis and first used the designation R_f.

But at this point interest in the technique seems to have died out. Little more is heard of it until the 1930's when Flood, in the U.S.A., investigated chromatography on paper impregnated with adsorbents, such as alumina. Liesegang, also in the U.S.A., carried out the first two-way chromatogram in 1943. However, no one took chromatography very seriously until it was put on a firm foundation by the team of Consden, Gordon, Martin and Synge in England in 1944. The latter two received a Nobel prize in recognition of their pioneer work on paper chromatography.

The work of the English scientists began with their studies on the separation of amino acids by partition methods on chromatographic **columns**. Not satisfied with the results they could obtain by this technique, they hit on the idea of using **paper** because they thought the bound water in the paper might possibly serve as the basis for a *partition chromatogram*. Using wool (protein) hydrolysates, they found they could bring about the separation of almost all the eighteen amino acids present by means of a single two-way paper chromatogram. By this stroke of genius, they changed the analysis of protein composition from a lifetime's work to a 2–3 day simple technique that could be carried out as a routine procedure in any laboratory.

The paper chromatographic techniques, as developed and published by these English investigators, were so elegant and efficient that they were very rapidly applied to the study of amino acids in fluids from many natural sources: plant juices, fermentation brews, blood serum, urine, etc. This was soon followed by application of the technique to the separation of other classes of compounds until today almost every type of compound known has been investigated, to a greater or lesser extent, by paper chromatography.

Medicine, in particular, benefited from the application of paper chromatography to laboratory examination of body fluids, and virtually no biological field has failed to derive some advantage from it. It has been applied in forensic chemistry to such things as investigations of inks on documents suspected of being forged, detection of doping of humans and animals, and analyses for poisons in cases of suicide and murder. In the art world, paper chromatography can quickly reveal the nature of the paints on a canvas to expose possible forgery. In biology, the near or distant relationship of animals or plants can be worked out by chromatographic examination of their tissues, and in biochemistry the study of metabolic pathways has been fantastically simplified.

In summary, it can be said that there is virtually no field of chemistry or biology in which paper chromatography has not made a substantial contribution to the furtherance of knowledge and understanding.

PRINCIPLES OF
PAPER CHROMATOGRAPHY

Why Paper Chromatography?

Nature abounds with complexities. Rarely is the chemist or biologist lucky enough to find the substance of his quest in readily available form. More likely than not it is a minute bit of a chemical hotch-potch that he is chasing. One of the scientist's major tasks is to unravel these complexities and reduce them to their simple components. In chemistry and biology this often takes the form of separation, isolation, purification and identification of scientifically interesting and important substances.

Uncommonly, this may be a relatively simple task. If, for example, his problem were merely that of separating powdered sulphur from iron filings, all he would need would be a magnet. The iron filings would cling to the magnet to make one pile, leaving the sulphur behind in its own pile.

But such crude methods will only work where the substances to be separated are of grossly dissimilar chemical and/or physical properties. As the substances become more similar, the methods required for separating them become more subtle and more complex. To separate and identify the metallic ions in a mixture of their salts, one had to go through the systematics of group analysis.

The same is true to an even greater degree of organic compounds. Glucose, a sugar, can be readily separated from phenol by shaking a mixture of the two with dry ether. The ether dissolves out the phenol and leaves the ether-insoluble glucose behind.

But it is quite a different matter if the problem is to separate and identify the several different sugars that one finds in honey; or the mixture of amino acids which results from the hydrolysis of a protein. There are no simple solvents the scientist can fall back on to do these jobs for him. In fact, these separations were

5

formerly considered so difficult that they were rarely attempted, except by a few dedicated scientists who were able and prepared to devote many years of work to a single analysis.

Paper chromatography was the ' open sesame ' which threw wide the doors to the speedy chemical analysis of complex organic materials. Also it made possible the separation and identification of microgram $(1 \ \mu g = 0 \cdot 000001 \ g = 10^{-6} \ g)$ quantities of substances in unknown mixtures. Contrast this with the thousand-fold larger quantities of materials required for group analysis.

What is Paper Chromatography?

Basically, paper chromatography is the technique of separation and identification of chemical substances by a moving solvent on sheets or strips of filter paper. A straightforward description of the technique is deceptively simple—because the mechanics of the operation is simplicity itself.

A drop, or ' spot ', of solution containing a mixture of the substances to be separated is placed, or ' spotted ', near one end of a piece of filter paper. The drop is allowed to dry, leaving a spot of the mixed substances. The end of the paper nearest the spot is immersed in a suitable solvent, without immersing the spot itself.

In *ascending* chromatography (Fig. 1*a*), the solvent is in a pool

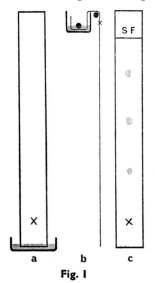

Fig. 1:

a—Ascending chromatography

b—Descending chromatography

c—A simple separation—a one-way chromatogram.

X = Origin, i.e. point of application of original spot of solution to be analysed.

SF = Solvent front, i.e. line reached by solvent at the end of the chromatographic run.

Fig. 1

at the bottom of a vessel in which the paper is supported. It rises up the paper by capillarity.

In *descending* chromatography (Fig. 1*b*), the solvent is in a trough, from which the paper is hung. It flows down the paper by a combination of capillarity and gravity. The latter, being a much smaller force, exerts an appreciable effect only in chromatographic runs exceeding 7–8 in. (say 20 cm).

In both cases the solvent flows along the paper, over and past the spotted mixture of substances. As it flows, it dissolves and carries along the substances from the spot, *each substance generally moving at a different rate from the others.*

The solvent flow is allowed to continue for a suitable length of time. The paper is then dried, and the separated substances are observed immediately, if coloured, or located as spots (Fig. 1*c*) by means of an appropriate chemical reaction. This technique is known as *one-way* (or *one-dimensional*) *chromatography* and the finished paper is called a *one-way chromatogram.*

What exactly has happened? Why have a number of substances which all started from the same point moved different distances and wound up as separate, discrete, coloured spots on the finished *chromatogram?*

A Resultant of Forces

As the solvent moves over the spotted substances, two opposing sets of forces get to work; the *propelling* forces and the *retarding* forces. The propelling forces act to shift the substances from their point of origin and displace them in the direction of the solvent flow. The retarding forces act to impede the movement of the substances by dragging them out of the flowing solvent and back into the paper.

The distance from the origin actually travelled by any substance in any given time is the *resultant* of these two sets of forces.

A reasonable analogy can be drawn to demonstrate this principle. All that is necessary (Fig. 2) is a smooth-topped table, a fan, two glass beads of similar size and weight, and some treacle (molasses). One glass bead is lightly dipped in the treacle, the other is left uncoated. The two beads are placed on a line drawn across the smooth table top. The fan is set up behind the beads and turned on.

There are now two opposing forces acting on the beads. The current of air set up behind them by the fan is the propelling force. The retarding force is the ' drag ' between bead and table.

The propelling force is obviously the same for both beads. The retarding force is not. For the uncoated bead it is the relatively negligible friction between smooth glass sphere and polished table top. For the coated bead it is the relatively considerable adhesive force between treacle and table surface.

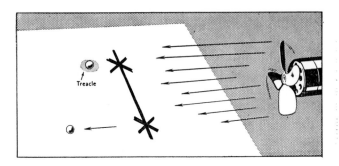

Fig. 2: See text.

The rate at which the beads will move along the table—and the distance moved by each in a given time—will be the resultant of the propulsive force of the air current and the retarding ' drag '.

What are the propelling forces and the retarding forces operating in paper chromatography?

The Propelling Forces

As a paper chromatogram is run, the two major propelling forces at work are the *solvent flow* and the *solubility* of each substance in the solvent.

    1. *Solvent Flow.* Barring other factors, when a solvent flows it carries all solutes along with it. If a substance being chromatographed were completely and instantly soluble in the moving solvent, e.g. sugar and water, and if no retarding forces were at work, it would move in the van of the *solvent flow* and be found at the solvent front—i.e. the furthest point reached by the solvent. Alternatively, if the substance were completely insoluble in the moving solvent, it would remain at the origin, e.g. sugar and ethyl acetate.

        Solvent flow, like the current of air in the analogy, is the same for all the substances in a chromatogram. Obviously, then, if the solvent were one which dissolved all the substances in the applied spot instantly and completely, they might all move together in the solvent front and finish up as they started: still together. This would get us nowhere, were it not for the other *differential* forces at play.

2. *Solubility.* One such differential force is solubility. Few substances have identical solubilities in any one solvent. The particular solubility of any one substance in the flowing solvent is a propelling force tending to displace it from the paper and to keep it moving along with the solvent. Other things being equal, the more soluble a substance is in the solvent the more rapidly it will move along the paper. In this way the more soluble substances from a spot will tend to outdistance the less soluble. Solvents are chosen to effect the greatest possible differential in the solubilities of the substances to be separated. As no one solvent may produce maximum solubility differentials for all the substances involved, resort is often made to two solvents, with different properties, run successively at right-angles to each other (Fig. 3). This is known as *two-way* (or *two-dimensional*) chromatography and the finished paper is called a *two-way chromatogram.*

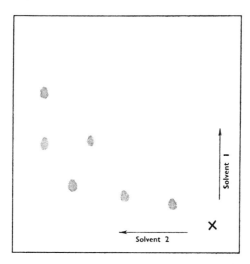

Fig. 3: Two-way chromatogram. The paper is placed in solvent I and run in the vertical direction. It is then dried, turned through 90°, run in solvent 2 and dried again. The resultant separation is called a two-way chromatogram.

The Retarding Forces

There are also two major retarding forces: *adsorption** and *partition.*

1. *Adsorption.* This force can be likened to the effect of the treacle on the glass bead. The coated bead tended to adhere to the table top and was thus retarded in its movement in the current of air. Loosely speaking, one could say the coated bead was adsorbed to the table surface.

   A similar sort of thing often occurs between molecules of one substance and the surface of another. Carbon is well known for its adsorptive properties. Its ability to adsorb many of the gases used in chemical warfare made it the prime ingredient of the gas mask.

   Cellulose, of which filter paper is made, also has adsorptive properties. The substances *spotted* on to the paper for chromatography may be more or less adsorbed on the paper. Adsorption is a reversible property and the cellulose will gradually release most substances back into the solvent as it flows over the spot.

   Adsorption is another of the differential forces—i.e. some substances are more strongly adsorbed than others and so the release of substances from the spot will vary from substance to substance. This again helps bring about a separation of the substances. As the chromatogram runs, the more strongly adsorbed substances are held back while the less strongly adsorbed move on ahead of them.

2. *Partition.* While superficially chromatography seems to involve the passage of a liquid solvent over a solid composed of cellulose fibres—i.e. the filter paper—the actual state of affairs is more involved. In fact, to a large extent chromatography depends on the presence of two non-mixing liquid phases. One, obviously, is the moving solvent flowing over the filter paper. The other is the bound aqueous phase present in the filter paper itself. A seemingly dry sheet of filter paper contains about 6–12 per cent water firmly bound to the cellulose. This is where partition comes into play.

* Two words which are often confused are *adsorption* and *absorption*. It is important to remember that adsorption means attachment to a surface. By contrast, absorption refers to one substance entering into the body of another—e.g. water into a sponge.

When a substance which is soluble in two non-mixing solvents is exposed simultaneously to both, it will partition itself between them. The amount found in each solvent will depend on the relative solubility of the solute in each. The degree of partition at equilibrium is known as the *partition coefficient* or *distribution ratio*.

This phenomenon is made use of in the process known as *countercurrent distribution*, the object of which is the separation of substances by virtue of their differential solubility in each of two immiscible solvents. (Immiscible solvents must be used in countercurrent distribution, since, neither solvent being ' bound ', the two solvents would otherwise become a single phase.) As this is analogous to the partition phenomenon in paper chromatography, we may consider countercurrent distribution in some detail.

Countercurrent Distribution

As already indicated, countercurrent distribution requires a two-solvent system in which the component solvents are immiscible and in each of which one or more of the substances to be separated has some degree of solubility. One of the solvents is distributed in a series of tubes, where it remains. Consequently, it is designated the *stationary phase*.

The other solvent moves from tube to tube according to a calculated pattern. Therefore, it is designated the *mobile phase*.

In practice a solute D (represented by 8 slant lines)—or mixture of solutes—is dissolved in the stationary phase S of tube 1 (Fig. 4, Stage 1). An equal volume of mobile phase M is added to tube 1, shaken thoroughly with S, and the two solvents allowed to separate, Stage 2. The solute distributes itself between the two solvents in accordance with its relative solubility in each. M is then removed and transferred to tube 2, Stage 3, while a fresh aliquot of M is added to tube 1.

At this point, Stage 3, the situation is as follows. In tube 1 there is solute in S, but not yet in M. In tube 2 there is solute in M, but not yet in S.

Both tubes are now shaken thoroughly and the two phases allowed to separate. The solute redistributes itself, so that it is again present in both solvents in each tube, Stage 4. M_1 from tube 2 is then moved to tube 3, M_2 from tube 1 is moved to tube 2, and fresh M is added to tube 1 Stage 5.   (continued p. 14)

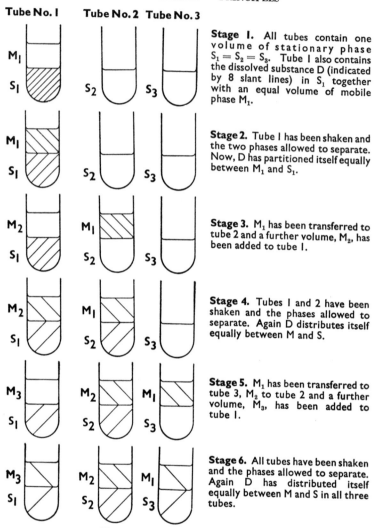

Tube No. 1   **Tube No. 2**   **Tube No. 3**

Stage 1. All tubes contain one volume of stationary phase $S_1 = S_2 = S_3$. Tube 1 also contains the dissolved substance D (indicated by 8 slant lines) in S_1 together with an equal volume of mobile phase M_1.

Stage 2. Tube 1 has been shaken and the two phases allowed to separate. Now, D has partitioned itself equally between M_1 and S_1.

Stage 3. M_1 has been transferred to tube 2 and a further volume, M_2, has been added to tube 1.

Stage 4. Tubes 1 and 2 have been shaken and the phases allowed to separate. Again D distributes itself equally between M and S.

Stage 5. M_1 has been transferred to tube 3, M_2 to tube 2 and a further volume, M_3, has been added to tube 1.

Stage 6. All tubes have been shaken and the phases allowed to separate. Again D has distributed itself equally between M and S in all three tubes.

Fig. 4: Countercurrent distribution.

The distribution of a substance in liquid-liquid partition. For diagrammatic simplicity a substance with a partition ratio of 1 has been chosen and this is indicated by the number of slant lines found at Stage 6 in each layer of each tube. At the end of the experiment the total amount of substance present in each tube must be determined. After three distributions this substance is found mainly in the middle tube because the partition ratio is 1. Obviously, in a 100-tube distribution, D would be found as a peak around tube 50.

Note that the numbering M_1, M_2, M_3 is in the opposite direction to S_1, S_2, S_3, indicating that the mobile phase is moving forward and across the stationary phase; hence the term *counter-current distribution*.

TABLE

The bottom line of each table shows the amounts of A and B respectively remaining in each tube after ten successive extractions with solvent M. Tube number is plotted against amount in Fig. 5.

Bold figures indicate tubes containing bulk of substance.

Substance A (20 per cent soluble in M)

Extraction No.	Tube No.										
	1	2	3	4	5	6	7	8	9	10	11
0	**200**										
1	**160**	40									
2	**128**	64	8								
3	**103**	76	19	2							
4	**82**	**82**	30	6							
5	66	**82**	40	11	1						
6	53	**79**	48	17	3						
7	42	**74**	54	24	5	1					
8	34	**67**	58	30	9	2					
9	27	**61**	59	36	13	4					
10	22	56	**58**	40	17	6	1	0	0	0	0

Substance B (80 per cent soluble in M)

Extraction No.	Tube No.										
	1	2	3	4	5	6	7	8	9	10	11
0	**200**										
1	40	**160**									
2	8	64	**128**								
3	2	19	78	**101**							
4	0	6	21	**92**	81						
5	0	1	9	35	**90**	65					
6	0	0	3	14	46	**85**	52				
7	0	0	0	6	20	54	**78**	42			
8	0	0	0	1	9	27	59	**70**	34		
9	0	0	0	0	3	14	32	61	**63**	27	
10	0	0	0	0	0	6	17	38	**62**	55	22

Now the situation looks like this at Stage 5: tube 1, solute in S but not yet in M; tube 2, solute in *both* S and M; tube 3, solute in M but not yet in S. The tubes are shaken once again and the whole process repeated. Stage 6 shows the resulting distribution of D, still represented by 8 slant lines. This goes on over and over again until the desired result is achieved.

What result *is* achieved? This can best be answered by looking at a particular case.

To visualize the effect, a crude calculation of two differentially partitionable substances can be carried out. In the Table p. 13 it has been postulated that substance A partitions itself 80 : 20 between S and M, whereas the respective partition ratio for substance B is 20 : 80. The starting material is taken as a mixture of 200 parts each of A and B dissolved in S of tube 1.

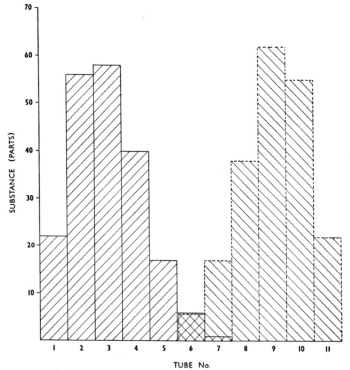

Fig. 5: The figure shows the distribution of the two substances A and B after ten extractions. The figure is prepared by graphing the amounts, or parts, of A and B (on the Y axis) against the tube number (X axis). Note that the two substances are almost completely separated.

Countercurrent distribution, as described above, is carried out and the amount of each substance present in each tube after successive extraction with M is recorded in the table. The calculations are necessarily rough, to avoid getting tangled up in endless decimals. Nevertheless, the result achieved is clearly seen in the Table and Fig. 5.

After only 10 successive extractions, B has already largely drawn away from A. The bulk of A is in tubes 2 and 3, with the peak in tube 3, and it is here completely free from B. On the other hand, B, with its greater solubility in M, has been carried further along: it is now predominantly in tubes 9 and 10, with the peak in tube 9, where it is completely free from A. There is still a small overlap in tubes 6 and 7, but this will be completely resolved in another extraction or two.

Separation of the two substances is well on the way, as is graphically shown in Fig. 5—and this after only 10 successive partitions of the substances between S and M. It is obvious that with continued repetition of the process A and B will be well and truly separated. Of course, in most cases the relative solubilities of two substances in S and M will not be so disparate, but the number of ' extractions ' will be many multiples of 10, so that good separations may none the less be achieved.

What does this mean in terms of paper chromatography?

Paper Chromatography as a Countercurrent Distribution Phenomenon

As we have seen, the integral water of the filter paper is firmly bound to the ultrafine cellulose fibres. These are intricately interwoven so that, in effect, the paper is made up of an astronomical number of microscopic ' cells '. As the water in each of these ' cells ' is stationary, each can be considered a minute ' tube ' in a countercurrent distribution system. The stationary water held fast in the tiny ' tubes ' is the S of the system and the mobile solvent flowing over the paper is the M of the system.

When a drop of sample in solution is applied to the paper and its solvent is allowed to evaporate, the solute dissolves in the water of the ' tubes ' which the drying drop overlies. As the moving chromatographic solvent runs over these ' tubes ', it picks up by partition some of the solute from the water there and redeposits some of it—again by partition—in succeeding ' tubes '.

As it moves along, it is followed by fresh M and, as in the tubes of our analogy, the process repeats itself over and over.

Consider the microscopic size of the 'tubes' in the paper and you will recognize in what a very short distance 10 distributions, such as we used in our table, will take place. In fact, thousands of partitions of solute take place between the S in the filter paper 'tubes' and the M, or moving solvent. Because of this, even small differences in partition coefficient between different solutes of a mixture lead to appreciable separations in the course of paper chromatography.

If, at this point, we go back to our countercurrent distribution table we can explain another phenomenon which we will observe in our experimental work. That is, although the drop applied to the paper is small, the spots which appear in the finished chromatogram are generally larger, of densest colour (or concentration) in the middle and fading at the edges. The reason for this becomes obvious when we observe how, by the very mechanics of countercurrent distribution, the solute stretches itself out over a series of tubes, with the higher concentrations toward the middle of the series and lower concentrations at either end. It is again fortunate that the 'tubes' in the filter paper are so tiny, because the solute can then be stretched out over hundreds of 'tubes' and still occupy a fairly concentrated and locatable spot on the filter paper.

Now it is also obvious why partition is a retarding force in paper chromatography. Because of its operation, solute picked up by the moving solvent is continually being returned to the paper and so retarded in its progress. And because such retardation is related to the partition coefficient of each solute, which will generally be different from that of other solutes, partition is also a differential force, working for the eventual separation of the solutes.

(In specialized cases, other retarding forces—e.g. van der Waals' forces, ion exchange, hydrogen bonding—are made use of to effect better separations of certain classes of substances.)

THE PRACTICE OF
PAPER CHROMATOGRAPHY

ASCENDING CHROMATOGRAPHY

Mechanics

Solvent is placed at the bottom of the tank to a depth of some millimetres. Test solutions are spotted at points along a line drawn near one side of a square sheet of filter paper. These are designated *origins*. The sheet of paper is then formed into a cylinder and placed in the tank, standing in the solvent, with the line of origin a short distance above the level of solvent. The latter rises up the paper by capillarity, passes over the test spots and causes the chromatographic separation of the test components. The paper is dried and the positions of the test substances, if not self-evident, are located by reacting with a suitable chemical reagent.

Apparatus (*see illustrations p. 18: specifications pp. 111–118*)

Tank - - - - -	*Part A*
Lid - - - - -	*Part B*
Filter paper, 25 × 25 cm -	*Part F*
Tongued clips (plastics) -	*Part G*
Dip tray - - - -	*Part L*
Pt–Ir wire loop - - -	*- in Part M*
Stainless steel clips - -	*Part N*

Paper

A 25 cm square sheet of paper is used. Draw a pencil line across the paper, 2·5 cm from one edge (Fig. 6). Beginning 3 cm in from one side, place *pencil* dots or crosses at 2 to 2·5 cm intervals along the line. Each dot may serve as an *origin* for a solution of test substances or for comparison standards. Under each origin indicate in pencil the substance to be placed on that origin.

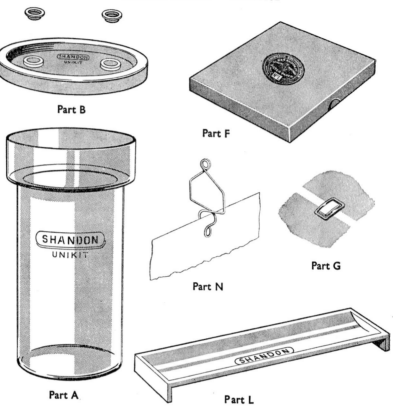

Part B

Part F

Part N

Part G

Part A

Part L

Solvent

Prepare a suitable solvent, as described for each experiment, in a graduated cylinder and mix thoroughly by inverting several times. Place 50 ml of the selected solvent at the bottom of the tank. To avoid solvent evaporation, the tank must always be covered with the lid, except when actually inserting or removing the solvent or paper.

Application of the Sample

To apply the test solutions to the paper, use the 4 mm diam. Pt–Ir wire loop, or a fine capillary tube, or the micropipette contained in Part M.

(*Note:* To clean the loop, flame with a Bunsen to remove organic substances; wash with water, before flaming, to remove metal salts.)

Take up the test solution in the loop (Fig. 6), or capillary tube, and apply to the paper to produce a spot not greater than 8–10 mm in diameter. If more test substance is required than is present in such a spot, allow the spot to dry and reapply similar quantities as many times as required, drying after each successive application. Drying can be accelerated (Fig. 7) by directing on to the spot the draught, cold or hot, from a hair dryer. Pencil an identifying symbol beneath each spot.

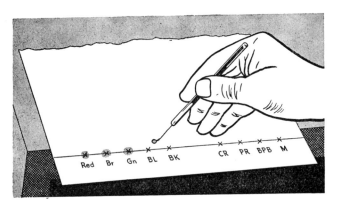

Fig. 6: Paper 25 cm square, marked for one-way ascending chromatography. The origins are on a pencil line 2.5–3 cm up from the base and are spaced 2–2.5 cm apart. The first origin is placed 3 cm from the side. The origins are coded in pencil, e.g. Red, Br., Gn., etc. Applying the sample: one drop of solution is picked up in the loop and touched on to the pencil-coded origin. The drop runs into the paper by capillary attraction. The origin line hangs over the edge of the bench in order not to contaminate subsequent sheets. It is good practice to cover the working part of the bench with a clean, larger, sheet of paper when ' spotting '.

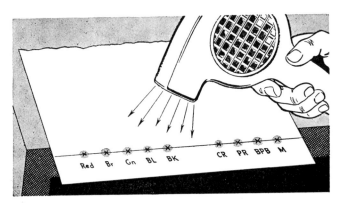

Fig. 7: Spots can be dried with a hair-dryer delivering either a hot or a cold blast.

Operation

Bring two edges of the paper together to form a cylinder (Fig. 8), with the starting line at one end. Fasten the edges together with the tongued clips Part G. The clips are made to keep the edges apart, as it is essential that they do not overlap.

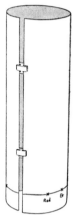

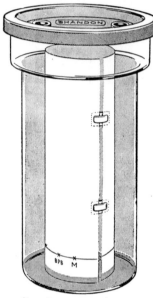

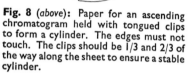

Fig. 8 (*above*): Paper for an ascending chromatogram held with tongued clips to form a cylinder. The edges must not touch. The clips should be 1/3 and 2/3 of the way along the sheet to ensure a stable cylinder.

Fig. 9 (*right*): The complete assembly for ascending chromatography. Chromatogram in the closed tank. Solvent is placed in the tank bottom and rises up the paper by capillary action.

Lower the paper cylinder, spotted end first, into the tank (Fig. 9) and stand it carefully on the bottom. Make sure it is standing freely and not touching the glass sides. The top of the solvent will be well below the level of the origin line on the paper cylinder. Place the lid in position, with the two holes in it closed by the polythene stoppers supplied.

The solvent immediately begins to flow up the paper by capillarity and moves over and beyond the dry spots at the several horizontally-aligned origins. The solvent rises rapidly and the separation of the components begins at once, in accordance with the principles already discussed. Separation may be complete within one hour and a 10 cm rise of the solvent. If the components are coloured, one can follow visually the chromatographic development and remove the paper when adequate separation is achieved. With colourless substances, it is necessary to become acquainted with each particular compound and mixture, and additional chromatograms may have to be run for longer or shorter periods to obtain the desired separation.

Drying the Chromatogram

Once the chromatogram has run to the desired stage, it is necessary to fix the components at the sites they have reached. This is done by removing the cylinder from the tank, opening it out, and rapidly driving off the solvent. To do this, hang the paper with a stainless steel clip, Part N, in a fume cupboard having a strong draught, or before an electric fan or hair dryer. The fumes or vapours, if they are noxious or inflammable, *must* pass into a fume cupboard. Mark the solvent front with pencil.

Locating the Separated Substances

When the test components are coloured substances, no further means of location is required. When they are colourless

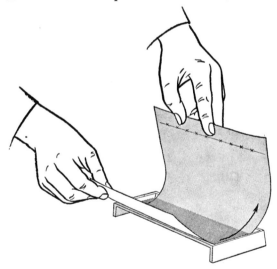

Fig. 10: Dip tray and the technique of dipping a chromatogram. Note that the chromatogram is held only on those parts of the paper where no separated substances can be present. The origin line is first immersed in the locating reagent and then the paper is pulled through in the direction indicated by the arrow. The corner of the paper is released by the right hand just as it arrives at the tray, is pulled through by the left hand and drained off at the tray edge. In this way, the whole paper is evenly wetted. With practice, the hands should remain completely dry.

C

compounds the dried chromatogram must be treated with a suitable reagent which will make the substances visible by reacting with them to produce coloured spots.

Two techniques can be used for treating the chromatogram with a *locating reagent*—i.e. either the chromatogram can be dipped through the reagent, or the reagent can be sprayed on to it. The UNIKIT provides a dip tray, Part L, which is used (Fig. 10) as follows:—

The paper should be dipped *once only*, from one end to the other, and immediately lifted from the tray. This is best done by taking one end of the paper in each hand, immersing the origin end into the dip reagent, pulling the paper slowly through the reagent and removing excess reagent from the end of the paper by passing it over the beaded edge of the tray. The spots may become coloured at once, or after the dipped chromatogram is heated to dryness at 105°C in a drying oven.

For permanent record, draw a pencil outline around those coloured spots which tend to fade with time (e.g. amino acid spots).

Sufficient reagent for the number of papers to be dipped should be prepared. Residual reagent should be poured away down the sink and the dip tray rinsed in water and acetone. Used reagent should never be returned to the stock bottle.

DESCENDING CHROMATOGRAPHY

Paragraphs marked with an asterisk are repeated from pp. 18–22 in order to facilitate reference to the basic techniques.

Mechanics

The dry trough is placed in the tank and supported on the tank gallery. One or two strips (one on either side of the trough) of test-spotted paper are hung from the trough with the end closest the origin sitting in the trough. An *anchor rod A* (Fig. 13) holds them in the trough. The paper passes over a second rod outside and slightly higher than the rim of the trough to prevent syphoning of the solvent. The solvent is poured carefully into the trough and rises into the paper by capillarity, passes over the *anti-syphon rod AS*, and is then carried down the length of the strip by a combination of capillarity and gravity. In its progress it passes over the origin, which lies just below the anti-syphon rod, bringing about the chromatographic separation of the test components.

Apparatus (*see specifications pp. 111–118*).

Tank - - - - -	*Part A*
Lid - - - - - -	*Part B*
Solvent trough - - - -	*Part C*
Glass rods - - - -	*Part D*
Filter paper, 30 × 10 cm - -	*Part E*
Dip tray - - - - -	*Part L*
Pt–Ir wire loop - -	*- in Part M*
Stainless steel clips - - -	*Part N*

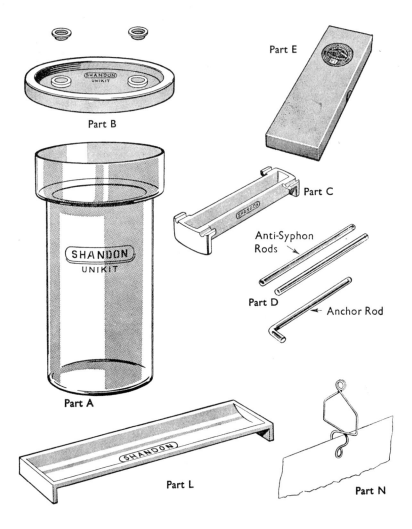

Paper

Take a strip of paper 30 × 10 cm. Starting from one end, draw pencil lines (Fig. 11) 1·5, 1·5, 2, 1·5 and 2 cm apart. Mark the origins with pencil dots or crosses, as previously described. Crease and fold the paper (Fig. 12).

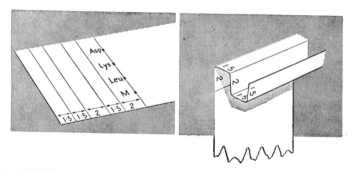

Fig. 11 (*left*): Paper 30 × 10 cm marked for descending chromatography. Five pencil lines are drawn at the following distances from the narrow end:—1.5, 1.5, 2, 1.5 and 2 cm. Origins are marked on the fifth line, 2 cm apart, samples applied and pencil-coded, e.g. M, Leu, Lys, Asp.

Fig. 12 (*right*): The paper is creased and folded sharply, as shown, at the first four lines drawn in Fig. 11.

Solvent

Prepare a suitable solvent, as described for each experiment, in a graduated measuring cylinder, by inverting several times. The solvent mixture is poured from the cylinder into the trough, after the papers are in position, care being taken to avoid splashing (see p. 25).

* Application of the Sample

To apply the test solutions to the paper, use the 4 mm diam. Pt–Ir wire loop, or a fine capillary tube, or the micropipette contained in Part M.

(*Note:* To clean the loop, flame with a Bunsen to remove organic substances; wash with water, before flaming, to remove metal salts.)

Take up the test solution in the loop (Fig. 6), or in a capillary tube, and apply to the paper to produce a spot not greater than 8–10 mm in diameter. If more test substance is required than is present in such a spot, allow the spot to dry and reapply similar quantities as many times as required, drying after each successive application. Drying can be accelerated by directing on to the spot the draught, cold or hot, from a hair dryer (see Fig. 7). Pencil an identifying symbol.

Operation

Follow the diagram and instruction in Fig. 13. When the paper is in position add 25 ml of solvent to the trough and close the tank with the lid (Fig. 14).

After the requisite length of time, open the tank and remove the anchor rod. Remove the paper by clamping it firmly to the anti-syphon rod with the index finger (Fig. 15) and lifting rod and paper out together. If much solvent remains in the trough, it can first be pipetted out, or the paper, as it is removed, can be angled so that solvent runs off it back into the trough. Invert the paper and hang by a stainless steel clip, Part N, while it dries. Exercise great care that drops of free solvent do not fall on the chromatogram during the removal of the paper. If two papers are in the trough, remove the upper one first.

*Drying the Chromatogram

Once the chromatogram has run to the desired stage, it is necessary to fix the components at the sites they have reached. This is done, after removing the strip from the trough, by suspending it with the clip, Part N, and rapidly driving off the solvent. Hang the paper in a fume cupboard having a strong draught or before an electric fan or hair dryer. The fumes or vapours, where they are noxious or inflammable, *must* pass into a fume cupboard. Mark the solvent front with pencil.

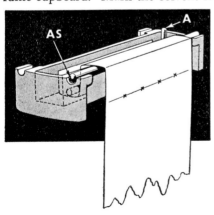

Fig. 13: Paper for a descending run hanging freely over the anti-syphon rod AS and held firmly in position by the anchor rod A. Two papers are usually placed in the trough, and hang down on opposite sides of the trough. Only one paper is shown here, for clarity.

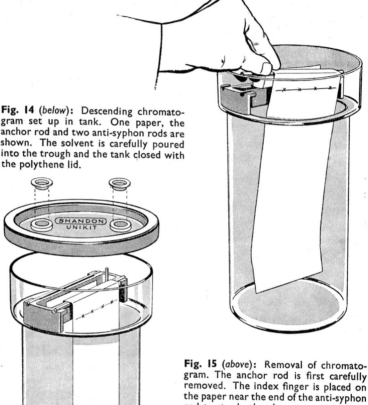

Fig. 14 (*below*): Descending chromatogram set up in tank. One paper, the anchor rod and two anti-syphon rods are shown. The solvent is carefully poured into the trough and the tank closed with the polythene lid.

Fig. 15 (*above*): Removal of chromatogram. The anchor rod is first carefully removed. The index finger is placed on the paper near the end of the anti-syphon rod to steady the chromatogram as it is removed from the tank. The rod is then lifted gently out of the tank. If two papers are in position, the uppermost is first removed. A clip, Part N, is affixed to the lower end of the chromatogram, which is then inverted and hung to dry. Take care that drops of liquid do not fall on to the chromatogram as it is being removed from the trough.

* Locating the Separated Substances

When the test components are coloured substances, no further means of locating is required. When they are colourless compounds the dried chromatogram must be treated with a suitable dye or reagent which will make the substances visible by reacting with them to produce coloured spots.

Two techniques can be used for treating the chromatogram with a *locating reagent*—i.e. either the chromatogram can be dipped through the reagent, or the reagent can be sprayed on to it. The UNIKIT provides a dip tray, Part L, which is used (Fig. 10) as follows:—

The paper should be dipped *once only*, from one end to the other, and immediately lifted from the tray. This is best done by taking one end of the paper in each hand, immersing the origin end in the reagent, pulling the paper slowly through the reagent and removing excess reagent from the end of the paper by passing it over the beaded edge of the tray (Fig. 10). The spots may become coloured at once, or after the dipped chromatogram is heated to dryness at 105°C in a drying oven.

For permanent record, draw a pencil outline around those coloured spots which tend to fade with time (e.g. amino acid spots).

Choice of Technique

Descending chromatography is the classic technique and is still widely employed, especially with non-volatile solvents. With highly volatile solvents, better results are obtained with ascending chromatography. It is important that the student become acquainted with both techniques.

R_f Value

The furthest point reached by the advancing solvent on the paper is termed the solvent *front*. This can be used as a reference point for describing the relative distance of travel of different substances in a chromatogram. The symbol used to designate this relative distance of travel is R_f, and is defined by the following equation (see Fig. 16):

$$R_f = \frac{\text{distance compound has moved from origin}}{\text{distance of solvent front from origin}} = \frac{x}{y}$$

As the denominator is always larger than the numerator, the R_f would be a decimal. For convenience it is expressed as a percentage by multiplying by 100.

Thus, an R_f of 50 would indicate that the compound had advanced half as far as the solvent front; an R_f of 25 would indicate a compound that had advanced only one-quarter as far as the solvent front.

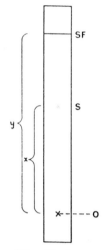

Fig. 16: A diagrammatised chromatogram.

O = Origin

SF = Solvent front

S = Substance

The substance was originally present at the origin X and has moved a distance x during the time in which the solvent front has moved a distance y.

The R_f is a useful figure because it is a constant when all conditions are exactly reproduced. As such, it is as characteristic and descriptive of a compound as is a melting point. Of course, the R_f of a given compound will generally be different for different solvents, but this is to the good as it is then possible to characterize a compound more specifically by quoting its R_f in several solvents.

Some of the factors which affect R_f values are the grade of paper used and the temperature at which chromatography is carried out. The temperature effect can be readily demonstrated by running identical chromatograms in triplicate, keeping one at room temperature, another in an incubator and a third in a refrigerator during the experiment.

If a chromatogram is to be used for R_f purposes, one should always mark the solvent front with a pencil line immediately the paper is removed from the tank, as it may subsequently be difficult to locate.

In some cases sufficient separation can be obtained only if the solvent is allowed to run off the end of the paper. In these cases it is obviously not possible to calculate R_f values. A reference substance is then used, with which the movement of other substances on the paper can be compared. The relative distance of travel is then referred to as R_x, x being the reference substance, and is calculated from the following formula:—

$$R_x = \frac{\text{distance the substance has moved from the origin}}{\text{distance reference substance has moved from the origin}}$$

In actual usage x is replaced by the first letter of the name of the reference compound, e.g. for sugars, where glucose is used as the reference compound, the expression becomes R_g. (See Note (i) Expt. C11, p. 59).

TWO-WAY CHROMATOGRAPHY

In many cases, chromatography in one direction is sufficient to bring about the desired separation of the components of a mixture of substances.

Where the complexity of the mixture makes for incomplete

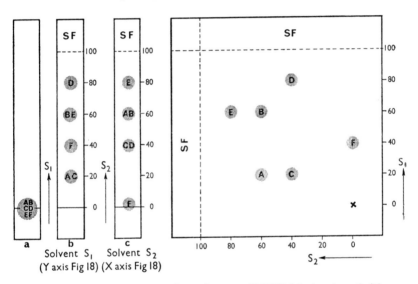

Fig. 17 (*left*): Take the mixture of six substances ABCDEF (**a**). In solvent S_1 (**b**), neither A and C nor B and E are separated. In the different solvent S_2 (**c**), CD run together, as do AB. Therefore, running these six compounds in either solvent S_1 or S_2, it appears that only four substances are present. SF = solvent front.

Fig. 18 (*right*): The advantage of two-way chromatography over one-way chromatography. In two-dimensional chromatography, use is made of the differing behaviour of the Fig. 17 substances in two different solvents to separate mixtures which are inseparable in either solvent alone. A square sheet of paper is ' spotted ' in one corner and run in solvent S_1 in the ascending direction, corresponding to the Y axis. The paper is then dried and rotated clockwise, so that the X axis becomes vertical, and a second run is conducted in solvent S_2, which is now also vertically ascending. All the pairs are now resolved and the chromatogram shows six spots, whose X and Y co-ordinates correspond nearly to those in the one-way runs of Fig. 17. It is interesting to note that F has an R_f value of zero in S_2. This is not a hypothetical case, as many examples of very similar substances are known, where two-way chromatography is essential to bring about a satisfactory separation.

separation of its components in a single solvent, *two-way*, or *two-dimensional chromatography*, with two different solvents, is employed to produce better resolution of the component spots (Figs. 17, 18). The two solvents are successively run in two directions at right-angles, drying the paper between runs.

In the UNIKIT apparatus provision is made for two-way chromatography only by the ascending method. If the dimensions of the apparatus were such that a square sheet of paper large enough to achieve a good separation could be used (as in commercial rectangular tanks) then two-way chromatography could be carried out also by the descending method.

Mechanics

The test solution is spotted near one corner of the square sheet of filter paper. Carry out chromatography by the ascending technique in the manner already described on pp. 17–22. Dry the paper, turn it through 90° and carry out a second chromatographic separation with a different solvent run at right-angles to the first. The paper is again dried and the substances located.

The effect is improvement of resolution through (*a*) increase of the available chromatographic path and (*b*) subjection of substances which may run together in one solvent, to a second solvent in which they run separately.

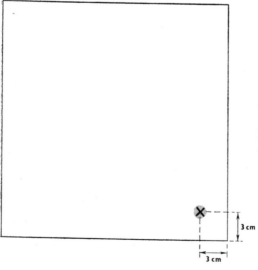

Fig. 19: Paper marked for two-way chromatography. Only one origin is marked, 3 cm up and in from one corner, and a code is written in pencil indicating the solvents used and the mixture separated.

3 cm

3 cm

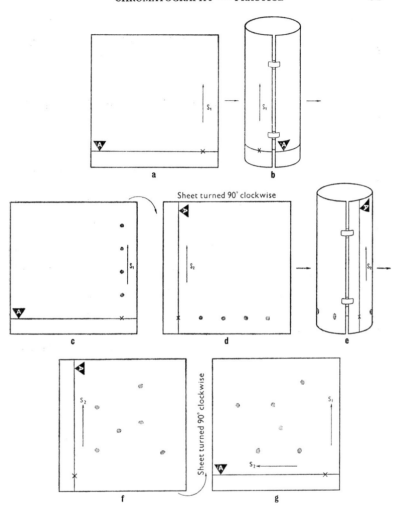

Fig. 20: Two-way chromatography. **(a)** Paper marked with origin and ' spotted ' for an ascending run in solvent S_1. **(b)** Paper coiled and held by clips in readiness to put into tank. Origin near bottom. **(c)** Chromatogram, uncoiled and dried after running in solvent S_1, and substances partially separated in the running direction, i.e. vertical. **(d)** Same paper turned clockwise through 90°, with spots previously separated now on a horizontal line near bottom. **(e)** Paper coiled and held by clips in readiness for a second ascending run in solvent S_2, in a direction at right angles to the previous run in solvent S_1. **(f)** Chromatogram, two-way, uncoiled and dried showing the separated substances. **(g)** Chromatogram from **(f)** turned anticlockwise through 90°. Note that the same chromatogram presents a quite different impression. For this reason a convention is necessary for viewing chromatograms, and in this manual (see also Book List, p. 110 ref. 2) the viewing convention is as in **(g)**, namely, the origin is in the lower right-hand corner with the first solvent separation in the vertical direction. The running conditions and solvents should be marked in pencil on all chromatograms.

Paper

Use a 25 cm square sheet of paper. Mark a single origin (Fig. 19) as a pencil dot 3 cm up and in from one corner.

Solvents

Choose two different solvents. Place 50 ml of one in the bottom of the tank.

Operation

Proceed as already described for ascending chromatography (pp. 17–22), placing the paper cylinder in the tank so that the origin is a short distance above the solvent level. After the first run, remove and uncoil the cylinder and dry the paper thoroughly (Figs. 20a–20g).

Empty the tank, clean and dry it, and place 50 ml of the second solvent in it. Re-coil the dried paper so that the two edges that were formerly adjacent now form the circular ends of the cylinder. Replace the paper in the tank, with the origin again a short distance above the solvent level, and allow the second chromatographic development to proceed.

When complete, remove the paper cylinder, uncoil, dry and locate the spots as necessary.

EXPERIMENTS IN PAPER CHROMATOGRAPHY

BASIC

(i) The practical experiments included in this section and the following pages are based on the UNIKIT and its accessories. Chemicals not included in the kit are separately listed in the Appendix and should be available before the experiments are begun.

(ii) For all experiments in paper chromatography follow the directions given in section " The Practice of Paper Chromatography ", pp. 17–32.

Experiment C1. Chromatography, ascending—the separation of the component pigments of commercial inks

Principle: (a) To demonstrate how the components in a mixture of compounds are separated by chromatography.

(b) To illustrate the technique of ascending chromatography.

Apparatus: See illustrations and list of parts, pp. 17, 18.

Running time: At least 1 hour.

Chemicals: Inks (see pp. 115–117).

Brown	-	-	-	*Part M200*
Royal Blue	-	-	-	*Part M201*
Scarlet	-	-	-	*Part M202*
Green	-	-	-	*Part M203*
Black	-	-	-	*Part M204*

Solvents: Either (a) *n*-butanol : ethanol : 2N ammonia (60 : 20 : 20 by volume) or

(b) water : saturated aqueous ammonium sulphate : ethanol (75 : 10 : 15 by volume)

Procedure: (see Figs. 6–10)—

- (i) Pour 50 ml of the chosen solvent into the bottom of the chromatography tank and replace the lid.
- (ii) Prepare a 25 × 25 cm sheet of paper with six origins. To each of five origins apply one drop of a different ink using a wire loop. On the sixth origin apply one drop each of brown ink and black ink. (This is for comparison with Expt. C5.)
- (iii) Form the paper into a cylinder and fasten with the tongued clips, Part G.
- (iv) Put the cylinder into the tank, taking care not to let the paper touch the glass walls.
- (v) Put the lid on the tank and run the chromatogram for at least one hour. Watch the initial flow of solvent across the origin and note immediate commencement of separation of ink pigments. Observe from time to time and note the continuous movement and separation.
- (vi) Remove the chromatogram and mark the solvent front with a pencil.
- (vii) Dry the chromatogram.

Conclusion:

Paper chromatography is a simple procedure for separation of components of a mixture. When the components are themselves coloured, it is possible to follow the course of the separation visually.

Note: Some pigments become invisible during chromatography and reappear on drying the chromatogram.

Plate 1: (facing p. 52)

Showing a separation of the component dyes of writing inks. One-way ascending chromatogram of the pigments in various inks. Butanol : ethanol : ammonia solvent. Observe that each ink contains a number of pigments; brown ink contains no brown pigment, the brown colour being obtained by the blending of other colours.

The majority of the separated substances appear as fairly compact bands or spots, thus showing that the solvent is suitable for these compounds. Some components have streaked or elongated in the direction of solvent flow; this indicates that the solvent has not coped too well with these compounds. It can be deduced that any one solvent will not necessarily resolve all the components of a mixture into completely separate and compact areas. As the chemical structures of the components of the mixture become more diverse, the chance of all components separating as compact spots diminishes. Compare the separations obtained with black and brown inks alone and when super-imposed. It can be seen that although the mixture looks almost identical with what would be expected by simply adding the two separations, it is not absolutely identical. The reason is that when many substances move with similar R_f's on the chromatogram they affect each other slightly, depending on their relative concentrations.

Plate 2: (facing p. 52)

Showing a separation of the component dyes of writing inks. One-way ascending chromatogram of the pigments in various inks. Water : ammonium sulphate : ethanol solvent. This solvent is inferior to butanol : ethanol : ammonia, as some components have streaked instead of forming discrete spots. Nevertheless these separations are quite adequate to differentiate two inks of the same colour, but from different sources, or of different compositions.

Experiment C2. Chromatography, ascending—the separation of pH indicator mixtures

Principle: To demonstrate the characteristic, invariable movement of a compound regardless of whether it is alone or in a mixture with other compounds which separate well from it.

Apparatus: See illustrations and list of parts, pp. 17, 18.

Running time: At least 1 hour.

Chemicals: (see pp. 115–117)—

Congo red	-	-	-	-	*Part M210*
Fluorescein Phenol red	-	-	-	-	*Part M211*
Bromphenol blue		-	-	-	*Part M212*
Light green Mixture of all three 2		·	-	-	*Part M213*

Solvents: Either (*a*) *n*-butanol : ethanol : 2N ammonia
(60 : 20 : 20 by volume)   or
(*b*) water : saturated aqueous ammonium
sulphate : ethanol
(75 : 10 : 15 by volume).

Procedure: (see Figs. 6–10)—

  (i) Place 50 ml of the chosen solvent at the bottom of the tank and replace the lid.

 (ii) Prepare a 25 × 25 cm sheet of paper and apply one drop of each of the three individual indicators and one drop of the mixture separately to four origins, using the wire loop.

(iii) Form the paper into a cylinder and fasten with the tongued clips, Part G.

(iv) Hold the origins over ammonia fumes to produce the alkaline colour forms of the indicators—i.e. the indicator anions.

 (v) Place the cylinder rapidly into the tank, before the indicators can revert to their free acid forms. This is important as the free acid form may travel with an R_f value different from that of the ionic form. Do not allow the paper to touch the glass walls.

(vi) Put the lid on and run solvent for at least one hour. Watch the initial flow of solvent across the origin and note the immediate commencement of separation of the indicators in the mixture. Observe from time to time and note the continuous movement and separation.

(vii) Remove the chromatogram and mark the solvent front with a pencil.

(viii) Dry the chromatogram.

(ix) Observe that the mixture of indicators has separated into its three individual components. Observe the different level reached by each indicator in the mixture and compare each with the level reached by the same indicator running by itself from one of the other origins. Note that the level is the same for each pair of indicators, regardless of whether they started alone or in mixture with the other indicators.

Conclusion:

When two or more substances, in a mixture with each other, are subjected to paper chromatography, each will run independently of the others and will proceed to the same point that it would have reached had it been run by itself.

Notes:

(i) If the indicators are run in the free acid form they may travel to quite different positions. This can be confirmed by experiment.

(ii) In this experiment the substances are well separated. However, in multicomponent mixtures of complex chemical substances it is likely that some of the components will, at the end of the run, be found to be located in similar positions (see Expt. C1, Plate 1 Discussion). Their R_f values will then be found to differ slightly from the R_f values of the substances run either alone or in *simple* mixtures.

D

Experiment C3. Chromatography, descending—separation of inks and indicators

Principle: (*a*) To illustrate the technique of descending chromatography.

(*b*) To note the similarity of chromatogram pattern to that of ascending chromatography.

Apparatus: See illustrations and list of parts, pp. 22–24.

Running time: At least 1½ hours.

Chemicals: (*a*) Inks (see pp. 115–117)

Brown	-	-	-	-	*Part M200*
Royal blue	-	-	-	-	*Part M201*
Scarlet	-	-	-	-	*Part M202*
Green	-	-	-	-	*Part M203*
Black	-	-	-	-	*Part M204*

(*b*) Indicators (see pp. 115–117)

Congo red	-	-	-	*Part M210*
Phenol red	-	-	-	*Part M211*
Bromphenol blue		-	-	*Part M212*
Mixture of all three		-	-	*Part M213*

Solvents: Either (*a*) *n*-butanol : ethanol : 2N ammonia (60 : 20 : 20 by volume)   or

(*b*) water : saturated aqueous ammonium sulphate : ethanol (75 : 10 : 15 by volume).

Procedure: (see Figs. 11–15)—

(i) Prepare two strips of paper, each 30 × 10 cm. On one, place each of the indicators and the indicator mixture separately at four different origins. On the second strip, place each of the inks separately at five different origins.

(ii) Fold the strips and hang them from the solvent trough, one hanging on each side of the trough and passing over the anti-syphon rod. Both strips are held down by the same anchor rod.

(iii) Place 25 ml of the chosen solvent in the trough.

(iv) Place the lid on the tank and allow the chromatogram to run for at least 1½ hours.

(v) Observe the initial separation of the coloured components of the indicator mixture and the various inks. From time to time, observe further the continuous running and separation of the coloured substances.

(vi) Remove the strips from the trough and mark the solvent front with a pencil.

(vii) Dry the strips and compare them with the chromatograms of the same substance attained by ascending chromatography. (Expts. C1 and C2).

Conclusion:

The relative order of separation of components in a mixture is the same whether ascending or descending chromatography is used.

Plate 3: (facing p. 53)

Showing a separation of the component dyes of inks. One-way descending chromatogram of the pigments present in various inks. Butanol : ethanol : ammonia solvent. Observe the close similarity between the ascending and descending chromatograms run in the same solvent (Plate 1).

Experiment C4. Calculation of R_f values

Principle: To define the relative migration rate of a substance under various conditions.

Materials: Chromatograms from Expts. C1, C2, C3.

Procedure:

(i) Measure the distance between the origin and the solvent front.

(ii) Measure the distance between the origin and the centre of each coloured spot.

(iii) Calculate the R_f value of each compound, using the following equation—

$$R_f = \frac{\text{distance compound has moved from origin}}{\text{distance of solvent front from origin}}.$$

Express your results as 2 place decimals and as a percentage.

(iv) Compare the R_f's of the three indicators as determined when each is run individually and when they are run as a mixture. The R_f of each component of the mixture should be equal ($\pm$ two units) to that of the corresponding pure substance.

(v) Compare the R_f's of the various compounds as determined by ascending and descending chromatography.

(vi) If the same mixtures have been run by the same technique in two different solvents, compare the R_f's in each of the solvents used.

Conclusions:

(i) The R_f of a compound is generally unchanged, whether it is run alone or in a mixture with other compounds.

(ii) The R_f of a compound is slightly different when run by ascending and descending techniques.

(iii) The R_f of a compound when run with one solvent is different from the R_f of the same compound when run with another solvent.

Experiment C5. Two-way chromatography, ascending—the separation of ink pigments

Principle: To demonstrate the increased resolving power of two-way chromatography over that obtainable with one-way chromatography.

Apparatus: See illustrations and list of parts, pp. 17, 18.

Running time: Two to four hours for each run.

Chemicals: Inks (see pp. 115–117)

Brown	-	-	-	-	*Part M200*
Black	-	-	-	-	*Part M204*

Solvents: (*a*) *n*-butanol : ethanol : 2N ammonia
(60 : 20 : 20 by volume)   and
(*b*) water : saturated aqueous ammonium sulphate : ethanol
(75 : 10 : 15 by volume).

Procedure: (see Figs. 6–10 and Figs. 19, 20)—

(i) Place 50 ml of the solvent (*a*) in the bottom of the chromatography tank and replace the lid.

(ii) Mark a single origin on the 25 × 25 cm paper 3 cm up and in from one corner (Fig. 19).

(iii) Place one drop of brown ink and one drop of black ink on the single origin and allow to dry.

(iv) Form the paper into a cylinder and fasten the edges with the tongued clips, Part G. (Fig. 20*b*).

(v) Place the paper in the tank with the origin at the lower end of the cylinder, being careful not to let the paper touch the sides of the tank and replace the lid.

(vi) Follow the movement of the coloured compounds visually until a satisfactory separation has been obtained.

(vii) Remove the chromatogram, open out the cylinder, mark the solvent front, and dry the paper. Place a pencilled number on each spot, in the order of its running, marking the fastest running number one.

(viii) At this point, the chromatogram may be stored until the next laboratory period. The tank is emptied, washed and dried.

(ix) To continue, place 50 ml of solvent (*b*) into the cleaned and dried tank. Replace the lid.

(x) Using the tongued clips, Part G, form the paper into a new cylinder in such a manner that the partially separated components now lie along a horizontal line 3 cm from one end (Figs. 20d, e).

(xi) Place the re-formed cylinder, spotted end down, into the tank, being careful not to touch the paper against the glass walls. Replace the lid.

(xii) The separated coloured spots now serve as new origins and you will observe that, as the second solvent ascends the paper, each of these spots moves upward at a different rate.

(xiii) Allow the chromatogram to run for 2–4 hours.

(xiv) Remove the paper, mark the solvent front, dry and examine the chromatogram.

(xv) Again number each spot with a pencil, in the order of its running, marking the fastest running number one.

(xvi) Compare the numbers indicating the running of each spot in each of the two solvents. Do you find any differences?

(xvii) Observe also the greater resolution of the individual compounds when separation can take place in two dimensions, by comparing with the chromatogram from Expt. C1.

Conclusions:

(i) The larger area available for chromatographic separation in a two-dimensional chromatogram increases the resolution obtained.

(ii) The order of running of compounds in a mixture with one solvent is usually different from the order of running with another solvent.

Plate 4: (facing p. 53)

Showing a separation of the component dyes of various inks. Two-way ascending chromatogram of the pigments in brown and black inks. Solvents: first, butanol : ethanol : ammonia; second, water : saturated ammonium sulphate : ethanol. One drop of each ink has been applied to the origin. Note that the ink separation obtained is what would be expected by plotting the R_f values of each pigment in each of the two solvents. If one-way chromatograms of these are available, then place them alongside the two-way separation such that each one-way run lies parallel with its equivalent on the two-way run and see that the theoretical plot of R_f's is correct. A number of the spots are diffuse. Contrast this with the compact spots obtained with the two-way amino acid separations in Plate 6. This is because the dyes are of much more diverse chemical structure than the amino acids and the solvents cannot cope with such diversity. In the majority of cases one is interested in the separation of a group of very similar substances such as a group of metals, sugars, plastid pigments, amino acids, etc.

Experiment C6. Chromatography, ascending or descending—the separation of metal ions of Group 3B (Zn, Co, Mn, Ni)

Principle: Location of colourless substances on paper chromatograms.

Apparatus: See illustrations and list of parts, pp. 17, 18, 22–24.

Running time: Two hours.

Chemicals: (see pp. 115–117)

Zinc nitrate - - -	*Part M220*	
Cobalt nitrate - - -	*Part M221*	
Manganese nitrate - -	*Part M222*	
Nickel nitrate - - -	*Part M223*	
Mixture of zinc, cobalt, manganese and nickel nitrates -	*Part M224*	

Locating reagent: Metal cations

Sodium pentacyanoammine-ferroate - - - -	*Part M270*
Rubeanic acid - - -	*Part M271*

Preparation: see (v) *below*

Solvent: Acetone : water : conc. HCl
(87 : 5 : 8 by volume).

Procedure: (see Figs. 6–10 or Figs. 11–15)—

(i) Place 50 ml of solvent in the bottom of the tank.

(ii) Prepare the 25 × 25 cm paper and place each of the metal nitrates and the mixture of the four separately at five different origins.

(iii) Form the paper into a cylinder and secure with the tongued clips, Part G. Place the cylinder with the spotted end down in the tank taking care not to let the paper touch the glass walls.

(iv) Close the tank with the lid.

(v) No observations can be made while the chromatogram is running because the compounds used are colourless in the low concentrations employed. The time is used instead for the preparation of the locating reagent required to transform them into coloured compounds when the chromatogram is finished and for performing experiment C6a. The metal cation locating reagent is prepared as follows:

Solution A
sodium pentacyanoammineferroate,
   Part M270 -   -   -   - 50 mg ⎱ Dissolve
water, distilled   -   -   - 20 ml ⎰

Solution B
rubeanic acid, Part M271   - 10 mg ⎱ Make satur-
ethanol   -   -   -   - 10 ml ⎰   ated soln.

    Mix 20 ml solution A with 1·5 ml solution B. Shake a few minutes. If not then a dark purple add more B and shake. Filter. Reagent is unstable. Must be made fresh daily and stored in cold.

(vi) After two hours, remove the chromatogram from the tank, mark the solvent front with pencil, open out and dry.

(vii) Fume the dry chromatogram with conc. ammonia until all smell of HCl is gone.

(viii) Pour the reagent in the dip tray (Fig. 10) and dip the chromatogram, using the technique previously described. The whole paper should turn a dark purple: if this colour change does not take place, then expose the wet paper again to ammonia fumes.

(ix) Immerse the paper in a large flat glass dish containing 2 per cent acetic acid in water.

(x) Rock the dish slowly until the background colour in the paper disappears completely, leaving deep coloured spots to indicate the positions of the metal ions. One change of the acetic acid wash solution may be necessary.

(xi) Observe that each of the metal ions has moved a different distance, zinc being the fastest and having moved the furthest.

(xii) Compute and compare the R_f values of each metal when run individually and when run in a mixture with the others.

Conclusions:

(i) Paper chromatography is a very simple technique for the separation and identification of colourless substances, such as the group metals, provided that their positions on the paper chromatogram can be located at the end of the run.

(ii) Each metal ion has a characteristic R_f value which does not change when it is in mixture with the others.

Notes:

(i) Unless highly pure or redistilled HCl and acetone and washed paper are used, a second ' front ' is apparent across the length of the paper, a short distance behind the solvent front. This is just visible before applying the locating reagent, but intensifies to a dark green line after the paper is treated with the reagent. Its cause has not been positively determined, but it is believed to be due to iron in the impure solvents and in the paper. The paper can be washed by running it in clean solvent and drying, before applying the sample for chromatography.

(ii) If time permits, this experiment may be repeated using descending chromatography.

(iii) Mixtures containing metals from different groups may also be analysed by paper chromatography, using various combinations of solvents to find those which give the clearest resolution. Metal ion analysis has many practical applications, such as in geochemical prospecting, the determination of trace elements in the soil, examination of alloys, etc.

Plate 5: (facing p. 68)

Showing a separation of the cations of zinc, cobalt, manganese and nickel (group 3B). Two ascending separations, one descending separation and one electrophoretic separation. The chromatographic solvent was acetone : water : HCl in both cases and the electrophoretic buffer was 1·5 per cent citric acid.

The three types of separation are shown side-by-side for comparison. Note that the ascending and descending runs are very similar, but not identical, whereas the electrophoretic separation is quite different, as would be expected from a different technique. Observe the variable green line in the ascending separations (see Note (i) Expt. C6).

Experiment C6a.   Chromatography, locating exercise, colourless substances.

Principle: To show that colourless substances can be located on paper chromatograms by the use of chemical reagents which react with them to form coloured compounds.

Chemicals: (see pp. 115–117)

Zinc nitrate	-	-	-	*Part M220*
Cobalt nitrate	-	-	-	*Part M221*
Manganese nitrate	-	-	*Part M222*
Nickel nitrate	-	-	-	*Part M223*

Locating reagent: Metal ions

Sodium pentacyanoammine-				
ferroate -	-	-	-	*Part M270*
Rubeanic acid	-	-	-	*Part M271*

Preparation, see Expt. C6.

Procedure:

(i) On a piece of filter paper place four pencil dots, 2–3 cm apart.

(ii) Place one drop of a *different* metal solution on each dot and allow to dry.

(iii) Hold the paper over ammonia fumes for a few seconds.

(iv) Dip (Fig. 10) the paper through the locating reagent, prepared as in Expt. C6.

(v) Immerse the paper in a glass dish containing 2 per cent acetic acid.

(vi) Rock the dish slowly until the background colour in the paper disappears completely.

(vii) Observe the appearance of spots of different colours at the points where the metal solutions were applied.

Experiment C7. Chromatography, ascending, two-way—to demonstrate the separation of plastid pigments (chlorophylls and carotenes)

Principle: (*a*) To demonstrate by one- and two-way chromatography the separation of the pigments of plants.

              (*b*) To compare the pigments obtained from different plants, e.g. those mentioned below, or from different classes of algae etc.

Apparatus: See illustrations and list of parts, pp. 17, 18, 29–32.

Running time: 20–50 minutes for each solvent (*a*) or (*b*).

Note: These pigments are labile and easily decomposed. All work should be carried out in diffused light. Chromatograms should be spotted rapidly and placed immediately into the tank. The run should take place in the dark, e.g. in a cupboard or in a cardboard box, and preferably in the cold, i.e. in a refrigerator or in a cold room.

Chemicals: Grass (other green plants, carrots, tomato purée, etc.).

Solvents: (*a*) acetone : petroleum ether (40–60°C)

              (10 : 90 by volume)

              N.B.—**Highly inflammable** or

      (*b*) chloroform : petroleum ether (40–60°C)

              (30 : 70 by volume).

Procedure: (see Figs. 6–10 and Figs. 19, 20)—

    (i) Pour 50 ml of solvent into the tank. Replace the lid. Allow about 15 minutes for some solvent to evaporate and to saturate the air space in the tank. In the remainder of the experiment have the lid off the tank as little as possible, as the solvents are very volatile.

   (ii) Take 1 g of fresh grass (or other plant). Cut the grass finely into a mortar, add a little sand and grind for 10 seconds. Place the ground material in a 50 ml stoppered tube, add 4 ml of acetone, stopper and shake vigorously for 10 seconds. Stand 10 minutes. Add 4 ml of water and shake.

  (iii) Add 3 ml petroleum ether and shake vigorously for

5 seconds. Stand and allow the solvents to separate, when the pigments will be found to have been almost completely extracted into the petroleum ether (upper) layer. The grass will be almost white.

(iv) Remove the upper, dark green, solution with a pipette.

(v) Prepare a 25 × 25 cm paper for one- or two-way chromatography.

(vi) Spot the solution on to the origin, using minute drops and keeping the origin diameter less than 0·5 cm. Apply as many spots as necessary (the solvent evaporates very rapidly), until a dark green spot remains after solvent evaporation. Do not use a hair dryer.

(vii) Form the paper into a cylinder and secure with the tongued clips, Part G. Quickly remove the lid and place the paper in the tank, taking care that it does not touch the sides. Quickly replace the lid. Allow the chromatogram to run the stated time, in the dark.

(viii) Remove the chromatogram and stand in air in the dark for one or two minutes, when it will be dry. Diffused light may be satisfactory if dark conditions cannot be achieved.

(ix) For two-way chromatography, empty the tank and wipe out any residual solvent. Place the second solvent in the tank immediately and replace the lid in readiness for the next run.

(x) For two-way chromatography, re-form the cylinder with the partially separated pigments forming a new circle round the cylinder and near the base (see Fig. 20). Run the chromatogram in the second solvent, remove and dry.

(xi) Observe the relative positions and colours of the different components. Mark their positions with pencil. Again work in diffused light or in the dark.

(xii) Observe the chromatogram under ultra-violet light, in a dark room or under a black cloth hood. Note that some of the yellow pigments absorb light and so appear as dark spots, while some of the green pigments fluoresce pinkish-red. Deterioration of fluorescence and visible colour occurs rapidly in the light.

Conclusions:

Paper chromatography, both one- and two-way, is a useful technique for separating the pigments of plastids in a simple, rapid manner. Adequate separations can be obtained in short solvent runs. This is advantageous as the pigments are labile and rapidly converted into derivatives. Conversion can be demonstrated by repeating the experiment in the light, or by first exposing the spotted paper to bright sunlight for a few minutes.

Notes:

(i) R_f values of these labile compounds are not reproducible, especially if quite different concentrations are applied, but the relative order of separation is always the same. For complete confirmation of identity it is necessary to examine the spectrum of the eluted pigment. Nevertheless, it is possible to compare the pigments from different plants and to deduce similarities and differences from the visible and the ultra-violet colours.

(ii) Because of the great volatility of the solvents, results and R_f values are very dependent on ambient temperatures. As both the acetone and chloroform increase the R_f values of all components of the pigment mixture, the student can vary the proportions in the solvent mixtures to suit local conditions.

**Experiment C8. Chromatography, ascending or descending
—separation of amino acids**

Principle: The separation and identification of individual
amino acids by paper chromatography.

Apparatus: See illustrations and list of parts, pp. 17, 18, 22–24.

Running time: At least 1½ hours. This experiment may be
combined with Expt. C9.

Chemicals: (see pp. 115–117)

DL–aspartic acid - -	Part M10
DL–leucine · - - -	Part M24
DL–lysine - - - -	Part M25
Mixture of DL–aspartic acid, DL–leucine, DL–lysine -	Part M43

Locating reagent: amino acids—

Ninhydrin   -   -   -   Part M272
Dissolve   200 mg   in   100 ml   acetone.
Keeps indefinitely in a refrigerator.

Solvent: Ethanol : water : ammonia soln. 0·880
(80 : 10 : 10 by volume).

Note:

The hands must be thoroughly washed before the paper is
touched, as amino acids are present in perspiration. The paper
should, at all times, be handled at the edges only, since finger
marks show up as confusing coloured spots after treatment with
the locating reagent.

Procedure: (see Figs. 6–10 or Figs. 11–15)—

  (i) Place 50 ml of solvent in the bottom of the tank. Replace
the lid.

 (ii) Prepare the paper, 25 × 25 cm, and place each of the
amino acids and the mixture separately at four different
origins.

(iii) Form the paper into a cylinder and secure with the
tongued clips, Part G. Place the cylinder with the
spotted end down in the tank, taking care not to let the
paper touch the glass walls.

(iv) Close the tank with the lid.

(v) No observations can be made while the chromatogram is running because the compounds used are colourless in these concentrations.

(vi) Run for a minimum of $1\frac{1}{2}$ hours, longer if possible. Remove the chromatogram from the tank, mark the solvent front with a pencil, open out and dry.

(vii) Pour the locating reagent in the tray, Fig. 10, and dip the chromatogram.

(viii) Heat the dipped chromatogram in an oven at 105°C for two minutes, or by holding over a hotplate. The amino acids form purple or blue spots. The colour is stable for some weeks if kept in the dark and free of acid vapours. For permanent record, outline the spots in pencil immediately after the colour is formed.

(ix) Compute and compare the R_f values of each amino acid when run individually and when run in a mixture with the others.

Conclusions:

(i) Colourless amino acids can be separated and identified by paper chromatography through the use of a locating reagent which transforms them into coloured spots on the paper.

(ii) The R_f values of amino acids are the same whether run individually or in mixture with each other.

Notes:

(i) Amino acids and mixtures can also be analysed by descending paper chromatography. In the case of complex mixtures, two-way chromatography is preferable. If time permits, Expt. C8 may be repeated using descending chromatography as described, e.g. on pp. 22–27.

(ii) The problem of the determination and identification of amino acids in mixtures was the stimulant for the development of modern paper chromatography. Since its discovery and application to amino acid study, paper chromatography has revolutionised the investigation of protein structure and of biochemistry in general. Amino acid analysis is invaluable for the study of metabolism, the examination of enzyme reactions and for the determination of characteristic abnormal patterns found in urine and blood in certain diseases.

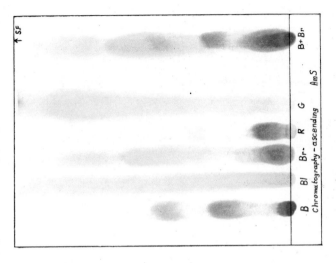

Plate 2: Expt. CI, separation of the component dyes of writing inks. One-way ascending chromatogram of the pigments in various inks. Water : ammonium sulphate : ethanol solvent. (see discussion Expt. CI)

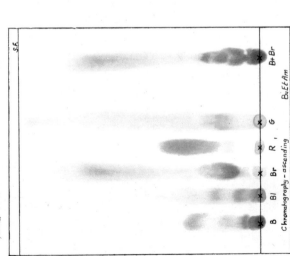

Plate I: Expt. CI, separation of the component dyes of writing inks. One-way ascending chromatogram of the pigments in various inks. Butanol : ethanol : ammonia solvent. (see discussion Expt. CI)

Plate 3: Expt. C3. One-way descending chromatogram of the pigments in various inks. Butanol:ethanol:ammonia solvent. Compare with the ascending run (Plate I)

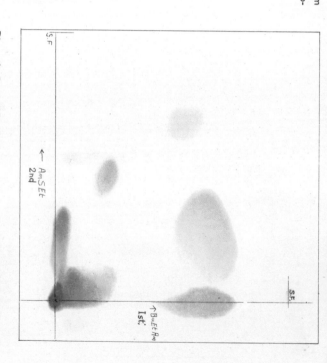

Plate 4: Expt. C5, separation of the component dyes of various inks. Two-way ascending chromatogram of the pigments in brown and green inks. One drop of each ink has been applied to the origin. Solvents, butanol:ethanol:ammonia, first; water: saturated ammonium sulphate : ethanol, second. (See discussion Expt. C5)

Experiment C9. Chromatography, ascending or descending —the separation and detection of amino acids in fruit juices

Principle: (*a*) To demonstrate the application of chromatography to the separation and identification of amino acids in natural substances.

(*b*) To show that more than one locating reagent can be applied to the same chromatogram.

Apparatus: See illustrations and list of parts, pp. 17, 18, 22–24.

Running time: Two to four hours.

Materials: Orange and lemon.

Chemicals: (see pp. 115–117)   *Spot these 4.*

DL–aspartic acid - -	*Part M10*	
DL–leucine - - -	*Part M24*	
DL–lysine - - - -	*Part M25*	
Mixture of DL–aspartic acid,		
DL–leucine and DL–lysine	*Part M43*	

Locating reagent: (*a*) amino acids—

Ninhydrin - - - - *Part M272*
Dissolve 200 mg in 100 ml acetone.
Keeps indefinitely in a refrigerator.

(*b*) sugars—

m-phenylene diamine -	-	-	0·5 g
stannous chloride -	-	-	1·2 g
acetic acid - -	-	-	20 ml
ethanol - -	-	-	80 ml

Solvent: Ethanol : water : ammonia soln. 0·880
(80 : 10 : 10 by volume).

Note:

The hands must be thoroughly washed before the paper is touched, as amino acids are present in perspiration. The paper should, at all times, be handled at the edges only, since finger marks show up as confusing coloured spots after treatment with the locating reagent.

Procedure: (see Figs. 6–10 or Figs. 11–15)—

(*a*) Preparation of fruit juices:

(i) Squeeze fresh juice from an orange and a lemon (or

tomato or similar local fruit), keeping each juice separate.

(ii) Centrifuge or filter a few millilitres. Keep 1 ml of each for chromatography.

(iii) To a second 1 ml portion of each juice, add 3 ml ethanol to precipitate most of the protein and salt.

(iv) Centrifuge or filter the alcohol-treated juices and keep the filtrate.

Method

(b) Chromatography:

(i) Place 50 ml of solvent in the bottom of the tank. Replace the lid.

(ii) Prepare the paper and mark with eight origins, numbering them one through eight.

(iii) On origin 1, place one drop of the amino acid mixture; on origin 6, one drop of aspartic acid; on origin 7, one drop of leucine, and on origin 8, one drop of lysine.

(iv) On origin 2, place two drops of the untreated orange juice.

(v) On origin 4, place eight drops of the alcohol solution of orange juice, drying after the application of each two drops and repeating until the eight drops are applied.

(vi) On origin 3, place two drops of the untreated lemon juice.

(vii) On origin 5, place eight drops of the alcohol solution of lemon juice, proceeding as in step (v).

(viii) Form the paper into a cylinder and secure with the tongued clips, Part G. Place the cylinder with the spotted end down in the tank, taking care not to let the paper touch the glass walls.

(ix) Close the tank with the lid.

(x) Run the chromatogram for 2–4 hours, remove the paper from the tank, mark the solvent front with a pencil. Open out and dry.

(xi) Pour the locating reagent in the dip tray, Fig. 10, and dip the chromatogram.

(xii) Heat the dipped chromatogram in an oven at 100–105°C for two minutes, or by holding over a hotplate, and observe the development of coloured spots.

(xiii) Carefully outline the amino acid spots with a pencil. Compare the position of the spots obtained from the juices with the positions reached by each of the known amino acids. This may identify some of the component amino acids in the natural juices.

(xiv) Note also that there are some spots from the juices which do not correspond with the positions of any of the three known amino acid spots. There will be a strong yellow spot, which is due to the amino acid proline, and a brown spot, travelling slowly, due to asparagine.

(xv) Treat the chromatogram with the *m*-phenylene diamine sugar reagent. (See Expt. C11, p. 59).

Conclusions:

(i) The juices of oranges and lemons contain free amino acids and sugars.

(ii) Chromatography is an excellent technique for separating and identifying the amino acids in substances from natural sources.

(iii) The application of a sequence of locating reagents to a single chromatogram increases the information obtainable.

Notes:

(i) This experiment can be repeated by the descending technique (see illustrations and lists of parts, pp. 22–24). Compute and compare the R_f values for each amino acid by each of the two techniques.

(ii) Compare the chromatograms of the pure juice with those obtained after alcohol treatment.

(iii) The amino acid content of different fruits will vary with the season of the year and the maturity of the fruit. It may, therefore, be found that 2 drops of juice is somewhat too little or too much for a single one-way chromatogram.

(iv) These juice extracts will be used for a number of experiments. To prevent bacterial or other growth, keep the solutions in a deep-freeze. If this is not possible, then, to each nine volumes of juice, add one volume of *iso*-propanol, as this is a most effective neutral preservative.

SUPPLEMENTARY
Experiments in Paper Chromatography

Experiment C10. Chromatography, ascending, two-way— the separation of amino acids in fruit juices

Principle: To demonstrate the application of two-way chromatography to the separation of amino acids in natural substances.

Apparatus: See illustrations and list of parts, pp. 17, 18.

Running time: Two to four hours; then overnight.

Chemicals: One of the fruit juices prepared for Expt. C9.

Locating reagent: amino acids—

      Ninhydrin -   -   -   -   *Part M272*
      Dissolve 200 mg in 100 ml acetone.
      Keeps indefinitely in a refrigerator.

Solvents: (*a*) Ethanol : water : ammonia soln. 0·880.
           (80 : 10 : 10 by volume)
      (*b*) *n*-butanol : acetic acid : water
           (60 : 15 : 25 by volume).

Procedure: (See Figs. 6–10 and Figs. 19, 20)—

  (i) Place 50 ml of solvent (*a*) in the tank. Replace the lid.

  (ii) Prepare 25 × 25 cm paper for two-way chromatography.

 (iii) Place 6 drops (or about three times as much as is necessary for a one-way chromatogram) on to the origin and dry.

 (iv) Form the paper into a cylinder, secure with the tongued clips, Part G. Place the paper in the tank, taking care not to let it touch the sides, and put the lid on. Allow the chromatogram to run for 2–4 hours.

  (v) Remove the paper, open out, and dry in front of a fan in the fume cupboard.

 (vi) Re-form the paper into another cylinder (see Fig. 20), with the partially separated amino acids forming a circle round the cylinder, near the base.

(vii) Place the paper in the tank containing the second solvent and replace the lid. Allow to run overnight (about 16 hours). See Note p. 57.

(viii) Remove the paper and dry it again.

(ix) Pour the locating reagent into the dip tray, dip the chromatogram, air dry for a few minutes, and heat in an oven at 100–105°C for two minutes to bring up the colours.

Conclusions:

Two-way chromatography is more satisfactory than one-way chromatography for the separation of complex mixtures.

Note:

Because the second solvent has run overnight, the solvent front over-runs the top of the paper and R_f values can no longer be measured. The individual amino acids can be identified by running mixtures of pure amino acids, Part M, simultaneously in a second tank.

Plate 6: (facing p. 68)

Showing a separation of amino acids. Two-way chromatogram of the amino acids present in fresh orange juice. Solvents were ethanol : water : ammonia followed by butanol : acetic acid : water. As the sample was not desalted, there is incomplete separation of the group nearer to the origin as the salts move to this area. Desalting would sharpen and compact the spots in this area (see Plate 9). Note the yellow proline spot and the brown asparagine spot.

The areas of the spots indicate the relative quantities of the different components in the mixture. Some of the substances may be peptides (amino acids joined in chains), as these also react with ninhydrin.

Experiment C11. Chromatography, ascending or descending—the separation of sugars

Principle: (a) The separation and identification of individual sugars and mixtures of naturally occurring sugars by paper chromatography.

(b) Determination of R_g values.

Apparatus: See illustrations and list of parts, pp. 17, 18, 22–24.

Running time: Overnight (see Note (iv)).

Chemicals: (see pp. 115–117)

D(+)-glucose	-	-	-	*Part M72*
D(+)-xylose	-	-	-	*Part M75*
Lactose	-	-	-	*Part M78*

Fruit juices as prepared for Expt. C9.

Locating reagent: sugars—

m-phenylene diamine	-	-	-	0·5 g
stannous chloride	-	-	-	1·2 g
acetic acid -	-	-	-	20 ml
ethanol	-	-	-	80 ml

Solvent: ethyl acetate : pyridine : water (55 : 25 : 20 by volume).

Procedure: (see Figs. 6–10 or Figs. 11–15)—

(i) Place 50 ml of solvent in the tank. Replace the lid.

(ii) Prepare 25 × 25 cm paper with eight origins and number one through eight.

(iii) On to origins 1, 2 and 8, spot one drop of lactose solution.

(iv) Allow the spots to dry spontaneously, or by blowing over them a current of air from a hair dryer.

(v) Spot a drop of glucose solution on to origins 1, 3 and 8.

(vi) Dry again.

(vii) Spot a drop of xylose solution on to origins 1, 4 and 8.

(viii) On to origins 5, 6 and 7, spot a drop of different fruit juices.

(ix) Form the paper into a cylinder and secure with the tongued clips, Part G. Place the cylinder with the origins end down into the tank, taking care not to let the paper touch the glass walls. Close the tank with the lid.

(x) No observations can be made while the chromatogram is running because the sugars are colourless.

(xi) Allow the chromatogram to run until the solvent front reaches nearly to the top of the paper or, preferably, overnight.

(xii) Remove the chromatogram from the tank, mark the solvent front with a pencil, open out and dry (see Note (i)).

(xiii) Pour the locating reagent into the dip tray, Fig. 10, and dip the chromatogram.

(xiv) Heat the dipped paper for up to 5 minutes in an oven at 100–105°C. The sugars form dark yellow-to-brown spots.

(xv) Compare and compute the R_g values of each sugar when run individually and when run in a mixture with the others.

Conclusions:

(i) Colourless sugars can be separated and identified by paper chromatography through the use of a locating reagent which transforms them into coloured spots on the paper.

(ii) The R_g values of sugars are the same whether run individually or in mixtures with each other.

(iii) Chromatography is a useful technique for the analysis of sugar mixtures.

Notes:

(i) If the chromatogram is allowed to run overnight, the solvent front reaches the top of the paper and continues to evaporate off the edge. In this case, no true front is available for the computation of R_f values. In such chromatograms, it is the practice to use an R_g value, based on the distance travelled by the glucose as the reference point, and computed by the following formula:—

$$R_g = \frac{\text{distance the substance has run from the origin} \times 100}{\text{distance the glucose has run from the origin}}$$

Thus, the R_g for glucose itself is 100. (See pp. 27–29 R_f value).

(ii) The sugar concentration of fruits varies with season and maturity. One drop of juice, therefore, may not be the optimum volume for chromatography.

(iii) The reagent should be examined by spot testing drops of pure sugar solution to ensure satisfactory application to the chromatogram (See Expt. C6a).

(iv) If time permits, the same sugars can be separated by the technique of descending chromatography, allowing the solvent to run for 6–8 hours. The R_f and/or R_g values can be calculated and compared with those obtained by ascending chromatography.

(v) The quantity of substance which can be detected on a paper chromatogram can now be considered. Briefly, the locatable quantity of pure substance depends on the sensitivity of the locating reagent. Some sensitive reagents, such as ninhydrin, will detect a few micrograms, whereas others, less sensitive, will detect only 10, 20 or even 50 micrograms.

The sensitivity of a reagent can be determined by spotting on paper serial dilutions of pure substances, drying and treating with the reagent. From the results of these spot tests, suitable concentrations can be selected and made up as standard solutions for future work. The sensitivity of the various reagents described in this Manual can be deduced from the concentrations of pure solutions in the set of Unikit Chemicals and Reagents, Part M, pp. 115-117.

Experiment C12. Chromatography, descending—the recovery of substances from paper chromatograms by ' elution '

Principle: To demonstrate a technique for the recovery of pure substances after separation by paper chromatography, by the elution method.

Apparatus: See illustrations and list of parts, pp. 22–24.

Running time: One hour.

Chemicals: (see pp. 115–117)
Indicator mixture - - *Part M213*

Solvent: *n*-butanol : ethanol : 2N ammonia
(60 : 20 : 20 by volume)

Procedure: (see Figs. 11–15)—

(i) Prepare 30 × 10 cm paper for descending chromatography.

(ii) With a micropipette, carefully streak the indicator mixture along the whole 10 cm origin line and allow to dry.

(iii) Place the paper in the trough and run as described in Expt. C3.

(iv) Remove the paper, lay it on a sheet of polythene film, while still wet, and, with scissors, carefully cut out the strip containing the bromphenol blue or phenol red.

(v) Quickly macerate the paper in ethanol. Observe that the indicator is washed off, or ' eluted ', from the paper and dissolves in the ethanol. Filter. Alternatively, the macerate can be poured into a glass column fitted with a sintered disc or cotton wool plug, and the dye washed through with alcohol.

Discussion:

What is the value of such a procedure? Quite often in chromatography, a spot is observed on a chromatogram which cannot be identified as a known substance. It is then necessary to prepare a larger amount of substance in a pure state for chemical analysis and experimentation. The chromatographic procedure is among the simplest for the isolation of substances. A paper 10 cm wide will hold up to 100 mg of substances in a single streak and so quite large amounts of material can easily be worked up in this way.

Conclusion:

Substances can be separated chromatographically and then recovered in a pure form by washing off, or eluting, from the paper.

Note:

In the case of sugar chromatography, a number of disaccharides appear on the chromatogram. These could be separately eluted, hydrolysed with dilute HCl and re-run to determine the constituent monosaccharides. A further use is in the quantitative analysis of a particular substance present in a mixture. The eluted substance can be determined by such standard methods as colorimetry, spectrophotometry, etc.

Experiment C13. Chromatography, ascending—separation of metal ions of Group 2A (Pb, Cu, Cd, Bi, Hg̈)

Principle: Location of colourless substances on paper chromatograms.

Apparatus: See illustrations and list of parts, pp. 17, 18.

Running time: 4–6 hours. (See Note at end of Expt.)

Chemicals: (see pp. 115–117)

Lead nitrate	-	-	-	Part M225
Copper nitrate	-	-	-	Part M226
Cadmium nitrate		-	-	Part M227
Bismuth nitrate	-	-	-	Part M228
Mercuric nitrate	-	-	-	Part M229
Mixture of lead, copper, cadmium, bismuth and mercury nitrates		-	-	Part M230

Locating reagents: metal ions:

    (a) *Sodium pentacyanoam-*
        mineferroate   -   -   *Part M270*
        Rubeanic acid   -   -   *Part M271*
        Preparation—see p. 45 and Appendix.

    (b) H_2S-saturated water, made alkaline with a few drops of ammonia soln. 0·880. Must be freshly prepared.

Solvents: (a) Ethanol : water : conc. HCl
        (90 : 5 : 5 by volume) or

    (b) *n*-butanol saturated with N HCl.

        Preparation. Add 50 ml of each liquid to a separating funnel, shake well and allow to separate. Draw off the lower layer and discard it; use the upper layer as the chromatographic solvent. If droplets of water remain in the upper layer, remove them by filtration.

Procedure: (see Figs. 6–10)—

    (i) Place 50 ml of the chosen solvent in the bottom of the tank. Replace the lid.

    (ii) Prepare 25 × 25 cm paper and place each of the metal nitrates and the mixture of the five separately at six different origins.

(iii) Form the paper into a cylinder and secure with the tongued clips, Part G. Place the cylinder with the spotted end down in the tank taking care not to let the paper touch the glass walls. Close the tank with the lid.

(iv) No observations can be made while the chromatogram is running because the compounds are colourless in the low concentrations employed. Part of this time should be used to make up the locating reagent, as described in Expt. C6, and to prepare the locating reagent (b) above.

(v) After the requisite time, remove the chromatogram from the tank, marking the solvent front with pencil, open out and dry.

(vi) Fume the dry chromatogram with conc. ammonia until all smell of HCl is gone.

(vii) Pour the locating reagent (a) into the dip tray and dip the chromatogram, using the technique of Fig. 10. The whole paper turns dark purple.

(viii) Immerse the paper in a large glass dish containing 2 per cent acetic acid in water.

(ix) Rock the dish slowly until the background colour in the paper disappears completely, leaving deep coloured spots to indicate the positions of the metal ions, with the exception of lead and sometimes of bismuth.

(x) Dip the paper in the H_2S reagent and note the appearance of the black lead and brown bismuth spots. Frequently a double spot is observed due, it is suggested, to the two ions Pb^{++} and $PbCl_4^{--}$.

(xi) Observe that each of the metal ions has moved a different distance.

(xii) Compute and compare the R_f values of each metal when run individually and when run in a mixture with the others.

Conclusions:

(i) Paper chromatography is a very simple technique for the separation and identification of group metals.

(ii) Each metal has a characteristic R_f value, which does not change when it is in mixture with the others.

(iii) No single locating reagent is suitable for producing coloured spots with all metal ions.

Note: Solvent (b) produces a much better separation but requires a much longer running time, i.e. overnight.

Experiment C14. Chromatography, ascending or descending, to demonstrate the ' salt effect '

Principle: To demonstrate the adverse effect on chromatography of increasing inorganic salt content in the original sample.

Apparatus: See illustrations and list of parts, pp. 17, 18, 22–24.

Running time: Chromatography, 2 to 4 hours.

Chemicals: (see pp. 115–117)

Mixture of DL–aspartic acid,
        DL–leucine and DL–lysine   *Part M43*

Locating reagent: amino acids—
        Ninhydrin -   -   -   -   *Part M272*
        Dissolve 200 mg in 100 ml acetone.
        Keeps indefinitely in a refrigerator.

Solvents: (*a*) *n*-butanol : acetic acid : water
                (60 : 15 : 25 by volume)   or
            (*b*) ethanol : water : ammonia soln. 0·880.
                (80 : 10 : 10 by volume).

Procedure: (see Figs. 6–10 or Figs. 11–15)—

(i) Mark seven origins. If using the descending method, apply 4 origins to one paper and 3 to the other.

(ii) On each of the first six, apply one drop of the amino acid mixture.

(iii) On origins two through six, apply 2, 4, 6, 8 and 10 drops of physiological saline (0·9 per cent sodium chloride), drying after each two drops.

(iv) Apply six drops of urine on origin seven, drying between each two drops.

(v) Run the chromatogram in the solvent.

(vi) Remove and dry the chromatogram and locate with ninhydrin in the dip tray (Fig. 10).

Conclusions:

(i) Increasing quantities of inorganic salts adversely affect the chromatography of amino acids (and other naturally occurring organic substances).

(ii) The urinary amino acid pattern is similarly distorted by the salts present.

(iii) The R_f of single substances is often considerably different in the presence of salt.

(iv) The ninhydrin colour reaction is not certain to occur in the presence of salt.

Experiment C15. Chromatography, ascending or descending, to demonstrate 'desalting' of biological solutions

Principle: To illustrate a simple method of 'desalting' extracts of natural origin.

Apparatus: See illustrations and list of parts, pp. 17, 18, 22–24.

Running time: Chromatography - - - 2–4 hours

Desalting   - - - - 1–2 hours

Chemicals: (see pp. 115–117)

Mixture of DL–aspartic acid,
DL–leucine and DL–lysine   *Part M43*

Materials: fruit juice or urine.

Locating reagent: amino acids—

Ninhydrin -   -   -   -   *Part M272*
Dissolve 200 mg in 100 ml acetone.
Keeps indefinitely in a refrigerator.

Solvent: Ethanol : water : ammonia soln. 0·880.
(80 : 10 : 10 by volume).

Note:

Although the technique for 'desalting' does not fall within the confines of this manual, a simple technique is described for the sake of completeness. No attempt is made to discuss here the nature or explanation of the procedure, but the method is described as an *ad hoc* recipe. However, for the reader who wishes to familiarise himself with the scientific explanation, the whole technique is discussed in Ref. 2, p. 110, and references 12 and 19 at the end of the relevant chapter. Accurate results can only be obtained by careful working and with understanding.

Alternative techniques are also described in that chapter, in particular Electrolytic Desalting, which is quicker and simpler, but which involves the purchase of an expensive apparatus.

Procedure: (see Figs. 6–10 or Figs. 11–15)—

(i) Take a glass tube, about 10 cm long by 1 cm diameter, and fit a glass wool plug or a sintered disc at the lower end.

(ii) Suspend, in water, a few grams of ZeoKarb 225 (Dowex 50), 16–50 mesh, 8 per cent cross-linked, and pour carefully into the tube to a height of 5 cm of resin.

(iii) Allow the resin to settle and the water to run through but do not allow the surface to become dry. (It is useful to have a tap below the tube.)

(iv) Carefully pipette 1 ml of urine or of fruit juice on to the resin and allow to soak in until 1–2 mm above the resin surface. Never allow the solution to run below the resin surface.

(v) Add 15 ml of water and allow to run through to waste.

(vi) Pour 50 ml of 2N ammonia carefully on to the resin and collect the effluent.

(vii) Take the effluent to dryness and redissolve the residue in 1 ml of water. The solution should now be salt-free and ready for chromatography.

(viii) Place 5 drops of neat and 5 drops of desalted urine, on two separate origins, drying after each two drops.

(ix) Run the chromatogram by the ascending or the descending technique.

(x) Remove and dry the chromatogram. Treat with ninhydrin in the dip tray (Fig. 10).

(xi) Compare the two separations.

Conclusions:

Inorganic salts distort the amino acid separation. Desalting of biological solutions can be carried out easily and completely with ion exchange resins.

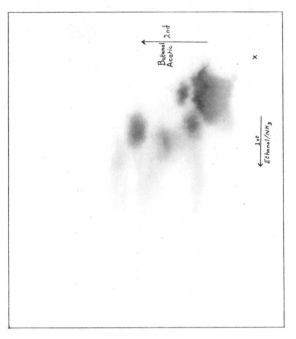

Plate 6: Expt. C10, separation of amino acids. Two-way chromatogram of the amino acids present in fresh orange juice. Solvents were ethanol:water:ammonia followed by butanol:acetic acid: water. (see discussion Expt. C10)

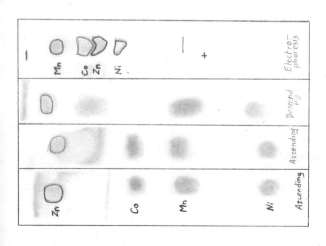

Plate 5: Expts. C6 and E9, separations of cations of zinc, cobalt, manganese and nickel (group 3B). Two ascending, one descending and one electrophoretic separation. Chromatographic solvent, acetone : water : HCl. Electrophoretic buffer, 1·5% citric acid. (See discussion Expts. C6 & E9)

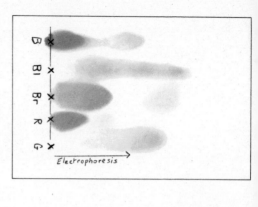

Plate 7: Expt. E1, separation of the component dyes of writing inks. One-way electrophoretogram of the component pigments of inks. Ammonia: ammonium acetate buffer. (See discussion Expt. E1)

Plate 8: Expt. E5, separation of the component dyes of inks by chromatography - electrophoresis. Two-way separations of the pigments present in a mixture of brown and black inks.

The first separation was by chromatography with the butanol:ethanol:ammonia solvent in the 10 cm direction and the second separation was by electrophoresis with ammonia:ammonium acetate buffer in the 30 cm direction. (See discussion Expt. E5)

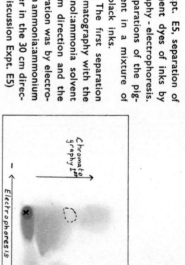

Plate 9: Expt. E6, separation of amino acids by electrophoresis-chromatography. Two-way separation of the amino acids present in fresh orange juice. The first separation was by electrophoresis in the pyridine:acetic acid buffer and the second separation was by chromatography in butanol:acetic acid:water solvent. (See discussion Expt. E6)

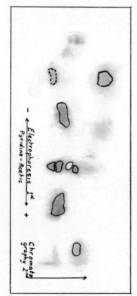

SECTION II

PAPER ELECTROPHORESIS

A Brief History of Paper Electrophoresis

The history of paper electrophoresis is even newer and shorter than that of paper chromatography. It might have been discovered in 1937 by König, had he appreciated the significance of a particular piece of work he did at that time, or had he published this work in something more widely read than the Portuguese journal in which it did appear. In this paper he described the separation of the proteins in snake venom by use of an electric current; but König himself has said that he did not grasp the potential usefulness of the technique on a wider scale and his article went unnoticed by other scientists.

It was not till 1946, therefore, that paper electrophoresis had its real beginnings. Again it was the team of Consden, Gordon and Martin who started the ball rolling. They reported the successful separation of charged substances by electrophoresis in silica gels. This led others to try paper as the supporting medium and almost simultaneously there appeared a spate of papers from various laboratories describing apparatus and techniques suitable for the separation of serum proteins by electrophoresis on paper. To name but a few of the early leaders in the field, there were Wieland and Grassmann in Germany, Durrum in America and Flynn in England (1948–1950).

The early workers were mainly intrigued by the possibility of diagnosing disease by studying the changes in serum proteins as revealed by paper electrophoresis. Even today this is still one of the major fields of paper electrophoresis investigation, but the scope of the technique is steadily being extended into almost every biological field, particularly when it is used in conjunction with paper chromatography as a two-way procedure. In fact, it can be truly said that the history of paper electrophoresis still lies before it.

F

PRINCIPLES OF PAPER ELECTROPHORESIS

Why Paper Electrophoresis?

Again we are concerned with the separation, at the microgram level, of substances which may not be separable readily by other means. When the substances in a mixture are ionizable, or when some ionize and others do not, some degree of separation of the substances may be obtained quite simply by subjecting the mixture in solution to an electric field. This is called *electrophoresis*, which is an incomplete form of electrolysis.

There are two major techniques of electrophoresis: *free electrophoresis* and *zone electrophoresis*.

In free electrophoresis the separated substances, being in solution, are free to diffuse the moment the current is turned off. This is a dynamic system and is usually assessed while actually in progress. It is, consequently, relatively complex and will not be further discussed in this Manual.

In zone electrophoresis the test substances are applied (Fig. 21) as a spot or as a streak of solution on a relatively large

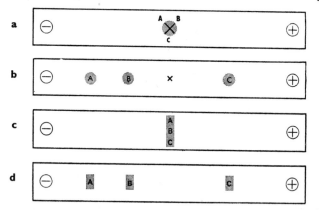

Fig. 21: The migration of ions. A mixture of three components A, B and C, is applied as a single small spot (a) or streak (c) at the mid-point of the paper strip (origin). As separation proceeds, (b) and (d), A and B, being cations, move to the cathode, and C, being an anion, moves to the anode.

supporting medium. The supporting medium is generally filter paper, cellulose acetate membrane, starch gel, agar gel, etc., referred to generically as ' stabilised media '.

Filter paper is cheap and is easy to work with and, therefore, is still preferred for most separations, although cellulose acetate has proved to be superior in many applications. Filter paper has been chosen for use in the electrophoresis experiments that follow.

As the test substances are present in confined areas on a supporting structure, it is possible to arrest and stabilize the separation at any desired stage by quickly drying or chemically fixing the *electrophoretogram*. The separated substances are then located, as in paper chromatography, by staining or by chemical reaction, which shows them up as coloured spots, or bands.

What is Paper Electrophoresis?

In principle, paper electrophoresis is very much simpler than paper chromatography. It is an incomplete form of electrolysis, in which the test substances are stopped along their paths of migration, instead of being allowed to continue their journey all the way to the attracting electrodes, as they would do in electrolysis.

Substances which ionise in solution have an electric charge. When exposed to the two poles of an electric field each ion will migrate to one pole or the other, depending on the sign of the charge it carries. As opposite charges attract, an ion with a negative charge will migrate to the positively charged *anode*; one with a positive charge will move toward the negatively charged *cathode*.

An ion derives its name from the pole to which it is attracted, not from the charge it carries. Thus, though the positively charged pole is called the anode, the positively charged ion is called a *cation* because it moves towards the oppositely charged cathode. Likewise, a negatively charged ion is called an *anion* because it moves towards the positively charged anode.

The concept of the nature of charged ions is derived from the *theory of valency*. This theory states that the bonds or linkages between atoms within a compound may be of two types: *electrovalent* and *covalent*.

In an *electrovalent* bond the electrons from the outer orbitals of one atom are transferred completely to the outer orbitals of the atom with which it is associated. Each thus assumes an opposite charge from the other, so that there is an electrostatic attraction between them. When such a compound is in aqueous solution the charged particles separate: the one (atom or radical of which it is part) wanders off *without* its transferred electrons, thus carrying a *positive* charge; the other atom (or radical of which it is part) wanders off independently, *taking* the transferred electrons with it and thus carrying a *negative* charge. These charged atoms, or radicals, are termed *ions* and the compound is said to be *ionised*. Examples of electrovalent compounds can be selected at random from among inorganic acids, bases and salts:

$$H^+Cl^- \qquad Na^+OH^- \qquad Na^+Cl^-$$

Organic acids and bases may also be appreciably ionised because of such groups as $—COO^-H^+$ or $—NH_3{}^+OH^-$. The H^+ of the former and OH^- of the latter wander off in aqueous solution, leaving the rest of the compound with respective negative and positive charges. Thus, acetic acid becomes $(CH_3COO)^-H^+$; while methyl ammonium hydroxide becomes $(CH_3NH_3)^+OH^-$. Ionisation is also a characteristic of organic salts such as pyridinium acetate:

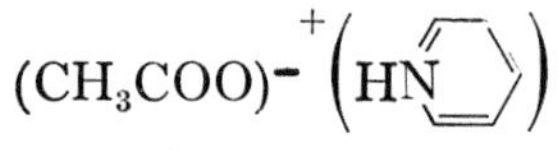

In a *covalent* linkage neither atom relinquishes its electrons to the other. It is a case of share and share alike. The two linked atoms indulge in a mutual sharing of paired electrons. Carbon is a notorious atomic indulger of electron sharing and the entire chemistry of organic compounds is primarily that of covalency. Thus, carbon tetrachloride is:

$$
\begin{array}{c}
Cl \\
\cdot\cdot \\
Cl : C : Cl \\
\cdot\cdot \\
Cl
\end{array}
$$

This difference between the types of valencies of sodium chloride and carbon tetrachloride is immediately manifest, if we expose each to a compound which reacts with chloride ions: e.g. silver nitrate, $Ag^+NO_3{}^-$. With the ionised Na^+Cl^- we get an immediate precipitate of silver chloride, but not so with covalent CCl_4.

The ionisation of electrovalent compounds provides the basis for electrophoresis. Electrovalent ions of different signs and charges, moving to opposite electrodes at different speeds, make possible the migration and separation of substances in electric fields. Uncharged covalent molecules show no electrophoretic movement at all.

To effect complete separation it is, obviously, desirable that all start together from a finite point, or narrow band, and that all have a long free path for their separating migration. This is another distinction between paper electrophoresis and electrolysis, for in the latter there is initial uniform distribution of solutes throughout the electrolysis bath.

Now the function of the paper in paper electrophoresis becomes apparent. It acts as the receptor for the point, or band, of dissolved substances and provides the path along which they can migrate. It serves yet another purpose. Once the current is turned off, the ions, freed from its marshalling influence, would begin to diffuse in all directions. If they are to be kept separated and discrete, it is essential that diffusion be halted quickly. On paper this can readily be done by drying the paper, thus fixing the separated substances *in situ* at the positions to which they have travelled during the electrophoresis.

In practice a suitable piece of filter paper is moistened with a buffer solution, to enable it to conduct the electric current to be used. A vessel is provided with two compartments, each containing the buffer solution. Into one compartment (the anode) is led the positive pole of the electric field; into the other compartment (the cathode) is led a negative pole or electrode.

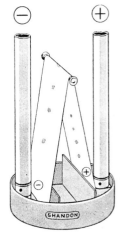

Fig. 22: Diagram of paper electrophoresis assembly (Vee support not shown). The electrode assembly contains buffer solution in the two outer compartments. One end of the paper strip dips into each compartment. Current is led into each compartment via the two electrodes (anode and cathode) and the circuit is completed by current flow along the paper. The mixture to be separated is applied at the apex and the substances migrate to one or other of the electrodes, depending on their charge.

With the current turned off—to avoid unpleasant electric shock—the buffer-wetted filter paper is so suspended (Fig. 22) that one end dips into the anode buffer bath, the other into the cathode buffer bath. A spot, or streak, of a test solution of the substances is then applied to the paper at its mid point.

Alternatively, the test solution may be spotted on to the dry paper, after which the ends of the paper strip are dipped into the respective buffer compartments. In this case, the buffer is allowed to advance by capillarity from each end toward the middle of the paper until the two advancing fronts meet.

The electric current is now turned on. Since the buffer salts act as conductors of the current, the buffer-wetted paper forms a conducting bridge between the two electrode compartments, and current flows across it, establishing an electric field.

The test substances spotted or streaked on the paper are caught up in the electric field. If they are positively charged they will start to move towards the cathode; if negatively charged, towards the anode (Fig. 22). Any substance without a charge will not be affected by the electric field and will stay put.

(*Note:* Obviously a *direct* current must be used. With an *alternating* current the electrodes would be constantly changing their signs. In sympathy, the ionised test substances would dash first one way, then the other, and end up by getting nowhere.)

Given a direct current, each charged substance will move steadily in one direction. But where will they get to in the end? If electrophoresis is allowed to continue long enough they will all end up either in one buffer compartment or the other. That is not the object of the exercise. Our object is to separate the test substances as discrete spots, or bands, within the length of the filter paper, so that we can identify them.

We can keep the substances within the bounds of the filter paper by adjusting the time we run the electrophoretogram. But how is separation brought about?

A Resultant of Forces

There are two features of an ion which are most pertinent to its electrophoretic behaviour; the size of the ion (i.e. the hydrated ion in solution) and the size of the charge it carries. These features oppose each other; the bigger the size the slower the ion will travel; the bigger the charge the faster it will go.

We can make an analogy with horses drawing two carts. In the first instance two horses have equal pulling power, but one cart is bigger and heavier than the other. The horse (charge) pulling the heavier cart (ion) will proceed more slowly than the one pulling the lighter cart. In the second instance both carts are of the same size and weight, but one cart is now pulled by two horses. It is obvious that the two-horse cart will travel faster than the one-horse cart.

Here again we have two opposing forces: size and charge. As in paper chromatography, where the substance ends up will depend on the resultant of the opposing forces acting on it. As this resultant will generally vary from substance to substance, each charged substance will move to a different position on the filter paper—in accordance with the sign of its charge, the size of its charge and the size of the molecule. Uncharged substances (or those carrying equal numbers of positive and negative charges) will remain at their point of origin. In this way electrophoretic separation of mixtures of substances is accomplished.

Additional Factors Affecting Separation

Other factors also play some part in the separation, such as the shape of the molecule—i.e. whether it is globular or elongated—and whether it is colloid (macromolecular) or crystalloid (molecular). Crystalloids being small, are relatively unaffected by the paper, whereas colloids are often partially adsorbed by the paper and may leave a trail tailing behind the main migrating band.

There are also factors deriving not from the substances themselves, but from the properties of the system in which the electrophoresis is carried out. These include:

(a) **Applied voltage and heating effect.** A strip of paper moistened with buffer has a resistance which depends, *inter alia*, upon the nature of the buffer and the amount of it on the paper, i.e. the 'wetness' of the paper. When a potential is applied to the paper current will flow. If V = volts, R = ohms, I = ampères the current strength will be determined by Ohm's law $I = V/R$ and will remain constant, if all conditions remain constant. The power consumed in watts $= V \times I = I^2R$.

The passage of the current for t seconds generates heat in the strip, expressed in calories $= I^2Rt/4\cdot18$. Heat produces evaporation of the water of the buffer, which condenses on the cooler walls of the tank. This evaporation is small at low voltages but increases as the voltage is raised and at high voltages the strip could become completely dry.

The ends of the strip are, however, immersed in buffer solution and during the drying more buffer enters the strip by capillarity. Since inorganic buffer salts do not themselves evaporate (organic constituents of buffers may do so) then, as more buffer is sucked into the strip, the concentration of salts increases and reduces the resistance of the strip continuously. From the equations, it is seen that, with a given voltage and a reducing value of strip resistance, the current increases linearly, but that the heat generated rises according to the *square* of the current. This square law increase obviously favours evaporation, which is the very state of affairs we do not want; we want to keep 'conditions', i.e. resistance, voltage, current, buffer concentration and temperature as uniform as possible. But we also want satisfactory electrophoretic separations in a reasonable time, with minimum diffusion.

Clearly, there is no ideal solution to this set of conflicting conditions. Rapid separations mean high voltages and consequently high currents; high currents produce heat and evaporation; evaporation results in changing buffer concentration, and variation of the environment during the run, which we have already said we do not want.

In practice, therefore, compromise conditions must be adopted. A voltage is chosen, which is as high as is practicable to bring about the maximum separation in the shortest acceptable time and yet does not produce excessive heat in, and thus evaporation from, the paper. With a paper 30 cm long and an applied voltage of 120 this equals 4 V/cm and the evaporation is then usually not excessive. It tends to become important in critical work as the voltage rises above this figure. Usually a potential drop of 2–10 V/cm is employed in view of the time factor, and any accompanying evaporation is tolerated.

There are, however, other steps which can be taken to ease, but not to solve, the problem, though their detailed treatment is outside the scope of this Manual. They include:—

    (*a*) Special electronically-controlled power packs which automatically maintain either voltage *or* current at a constant, predetermined value, despite the unavoidable resistance changes in the paper due to evaporation. The Shandon VOKAM power supply is an example, of which details will be sent on application to the publishers.

(b) The clamping of the wet paper between electrically non-conducting, but thermally good-conducting, cooled or refrigerated flat plates. By this means heat is rapidly removed from the paper and evaporation is reduced.

(c) Total immersion of the strip in an inert organic solvent. Methods (b) and (c) have found wide application in High Voltage Electrophoresis, where the potentials used may rise to $10 \text{ k}V$ (10,000 volts) on paper strips one metre long ($= 100 \text{ } V/\text{cm}$).

(b) **Buffer concentration.** Buffer concentration, particularly when non-volatile salts are used, greatly affects ion mobility. In general, increasing buffer concentration results in decreasing ion mobility. Also, increasing buffer concentration means increasing conductivity and, consequently, greater heating, with the undesirable effects described above.

(c) **Buffer pH.** The pH of the buffer may have a considerable effect on the substances to be separated, particularly when these are *ampholytes*—i.e. substances which may carry both positive and negative charges. Consider an amino acid, or protein, which carries both the —COO^- H^+ and —$NH_3^+OH^-$ groups and can, therefore, exist in the following forms:

$$H_3N^+\!\!-\!\!\overset{\displaystyle R}{\underset{|}{C}}\!H\!-\!\!COOH \underset{H^+}{\overset{OH^-}{\rightleftharpoons}} H_3N^+\!\!-\!\!\overset{\displaystyle R}{\underset{|}{C}}\!H\!-\!\!COO^- \underset{H^+}{\overset{OH^-}{\rightleftharpoons}} H_2N\!\!-\!\!\overset{\displaystyle R}{\underset{|}{C}}\!H\!-\!\!COO^-$$

| cation at acid pH | externally neutral molecule at iso-electric point | anion at alkaline pH |

It follows that such a substance can, by a suitable choice of buffer pH, be made to migrate to the anode or the cathode or to remain at the origin. Conversely, the *iso-electric* point of an amino acid or protein can be determined experimentally by running the experiment at a number of different pH's and determining the pH at which it is drawn toward neither the anode nor the cathode. However, in such experiments the fourth system-factor must be taken into account, and this is:—

(d) **Electro-osmotic effect.** When two different substances, such as filter paper and water, come into contact they may become relatively charged with respect to each other. In this case the water becomes positive relative to the paper. As the paper is fixed while the water is free to move, when an electric current is applied the water streams towards the cathode, carrying with it, of course, all dissolved substances. Thus, an overall movement of all dissolved substances, whether ionic or not, occurs in the direction of the cathode. The dissolved substances are then like swimmers in a stream. Those swimming with the stream current will be speeded on their way downstream. Those swimming upstream at a rate less than the water current will be slowly carried downstream. Those swimming upstream at the same rate as the water flow will not move at all. But those swimming upstream strongly will manage to move ahead despite the opposite flow of the stream. Going back to our dissolved substances in the cathodically-moving electro-osmotic stream, we can see that, though the overall movement may be toward the cathode, those substances with strong enough negative charges will still manage to move against the current and travel anodically. However, substances carrying no net charge, such as our ampholyte at its iso-electric point, will not remain at the origin, but will be carried slowly towards the cathode by the electro-osmotic stream.

Electro-osmotic flow can be demonstrated, and its rate measured, by the use of a non-ionised compound which will not migrate in the electric field. Usually, a compound of molecular size similar to that of the migrating substance is chosen and placed on an adjacent origin. At the end of the experiment, the non-ionised molecule will be found to have moved a slight distance from the origin, due to the electro-osmotic flow.

For small ions, glucose or urea is generally used and for larger ions, dextran or polyvinyl pyrrolidone. The electro-osmotic effect is generally ignored in electrophoresis, as the interest of most workers is in obtaining good, reproducible separations. It must not be confused with the syphoning effect which would result if the buffer levels in the two electrode compartments were unequal.

(e) **Diffusion effects.** If a single substance is spotted on a buffer-wetted paper, but no potential is applied, then the substance will slowly diffuse out into the body of the wet paper. The rate of diffusion depends, to some extent, on the molecular size of the diffusing ion and is comparatively slow with time. Diffusion also occurs after a potential has been applied to the paper and while the substance is in the process of migrating. The greater the potential drop (volts/cm), the shorter is the time of the experiment and it follows, therefore, that the less is the diffusion effect.

Normally, diffusion is not a problem in electrophoresis on stabilised media, i.e. in zone electrophoresis (see Why Paper Electrophoresis? pp. 70, 71). Nevertheless care must be taken to apply the potential as soon as possible after the substances are spotted or streaked on the origins and to dry the paper rapidly and with as little delay as possible, after the current is switched off.

Migration Velocity

There is no simple electrophoretic expression equivalent to the chromatographic R_f. The *migration velocity* has been defined as the movement of the substance in cm/sec at a potential drop of 1 V/cm. Allowance must be made for electro-osmotic flow.

The numerical value of the migration velocity is rarely used, as most workers are interested in separation of the components of a mixture with a view to their identification. It is thus usual to ascertain experimentally the optimum conditions and in quoting results, either to state the movement of the ions in cm, the voltage employed and the time of its duration, or to use a standard mixture run simultaneously for direct comparison.

A theoretical discussion of migration velocity is outside the scope of this Manual; a full mathematical treatment will be found in refs. 3 and 7 in the Book List p. 110.

Power Supply

A direct current is necessary for electrophoresis. It can be obtained in two main ways. The simplest procedure is to use high-tension dry batteries, coupled together, if necessary, to provide 250–300 volts. A mains power supply has been developed specially for use with the Shandon UNIKIT.

The UNIKIT Mains Power Supply (*see illustration p. 118*)

The UNIKIT mains power supply is specially made for the experiments which follow. It is foolproof, safe, and is an ideal unit for schools and colleges. It incorporates a double-wound transformer, with a metal rectifier and current-limiting resistors. It provides, from each of four pairs of output sockets, an open-circuit voltage of 350V, which is sufficiently high to enable most of the experiments to be completed in 1–2 hours. It is designed to pass a current of not more than 10 mA, even if short-circuited at any of the four outputs and cannot, therefore, be burned out by careless student use. All the experimental conditions have been designed with these figures in view.

THE PRACTICE OF
PAPER ELECTROPHORESIS

Mechanics

A strip of paper is wetted by dipping it in a buffer solution and excess buffer is blotted off between sheets of clean filter paper. Wetting with a buffer solution is necessary, as otherwise the resistance of the paper would be too great and no current would flow. Buffer is also used to maintain reasonably constant conditions of pH during the experiment. The strip is then placed between two buffer-containing electrode compartments, one end dipping into the anode compartment and the other into the cathode compartment. The mixture of substances to be separated electrophoretically is applied at a point on the paper mid-way between the electrode compartments, called the *origin*. The current is turned on. The ionised substances in the test mixture are then attracted to the electrode compartment of opposite charge and start to move along the paper in that direction. After a suitable length of time, the current is switched off and the strip of paper removed and dried as quickly as possible in a hot oven or in front of an infra-red lamp. The separated substances are then located as described under Chromatography (see p. 22).

The above electrophoresis procedure is a one-way separation corresponding to a one-way chromatogram. The finished paper is an *electrophoretogram*.

Apparatus

Tank - - - - -	*Part A*
Lid - - - - - -	*Part B*
Filter paper, 30 × 10 cm - -	*Part E*
Electrophoresis assembly - -	*Part H*
Glass rod - - - - -	*Part J*
Leads, electrical - - -	*Part K*
Dip tray - - - - -	*Part L*
Stainless steel clips - - -	*Part N*
Power supply (or batteries)	

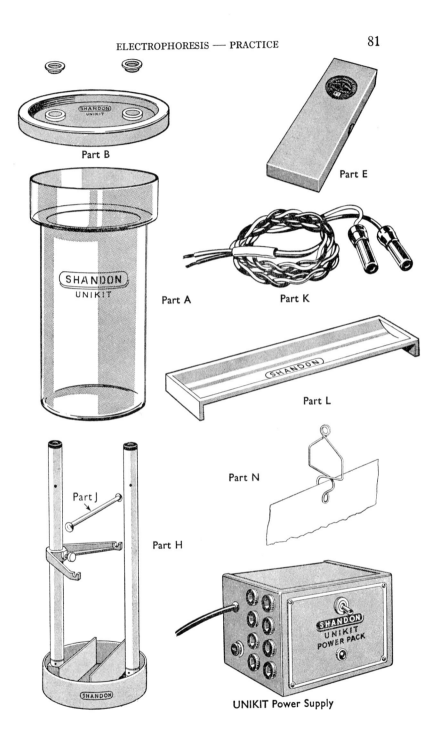

Part B

Part E

Part A

Part K

Part L

Part J

Part H

Part N

UNIKIT Power Supply

Paper

A strip of paper, 30 × 10 cm, is used. Draw a faint pencil line across the paper 15 cm from one end. Individual origins 2 cm apart on the line can be indicated by pencil dots or crosses (Fig. 23). Mark the positive end + and label the origins.

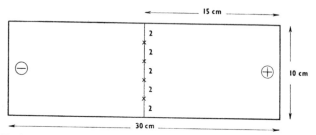

Fig. 23: Marking the paper for electrophoresis. A thin pencil line is drawn 15 cm from one end of the paper. Avoid heavy pressure and scoring the paper. One or more origins are marked as shown, 2 cm apart. The positive and negative ends should be marked.

Electrode Assembly

The base unit is moulded as a three-compartment vessel of polythene. Threaded sockets are provided so that the two polythene electrode pillars screw in vertically. The pillars are hollow to allow the electrodes to run the full length of the tube; the parts immersed in the buffer solution are platinised. At the lower end of each pillar are four holes and a circular groove; and at the upper end an air vent hole. The threaded sockets have, near their ends, a slit, which permits the circulation of buffer solution through the four pillar holes and past the platinised electrodes.

The apparatus is assembled as follows (Figs. 24, 25):—

  (i) The electrodes are screwed, firmly but carefully, into the base vessel.

 (ii) The Vee-shaped paper holder is placed on one electrode and clamped about 15 cm above the base. The glass rod with button ends is placed across it, parallel to the partitions in the base.

(iii) Buffer is added to each compartment, until it reaches the height of the groove on the electrode. As this height is above that of the four holes, buffer passes into contact with the platinised electrodes. About 100 ml buffer is required in total, equal volumes in each compartment to prevent syphoning from one compartment to the other, via the paper strip.

(iv) One or more origins are marked on the paper.

Application of sample and buffer to the paper:

Two types of ' spot ' are employed—drops and streaks. Drops are simple to use where many origins are required and where two-way separations are to be carried out. They are also simpler where the initial concentration of dissolved substances is low and where, therefore, it may be necessary to apply successively a number of drops to one origin, drying between the application of each drop.

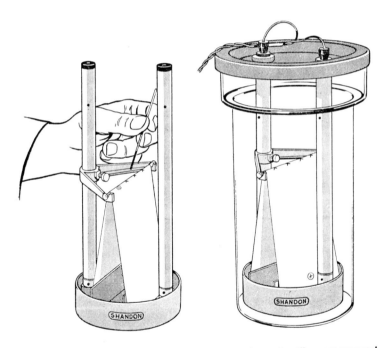

Fig. 24 (*left*): The electrophoresis assembly. The electrode pillars are screwed into their respective positions, the Vee support is clamped to one pillar and the button-ended paper support rod, Part J, rests in the Vee. The sample solution is taken up in a capillary tube or a micropipette and applied as described. The hand can be steadied by resting it lightly on the Vee support.

Fig. 25 (*right*): Electrophoresis: the complete apparatus ready for a run. The electrode assembly has been lowered carefully into the tank, the lid placed in position and the terminals inserted into the electrodes. The current is then switched on.

Streaks are used for the better resolution of close-running substances, where a circular origin may produce spots overlapping after the run (See p. 102, Notes (ii) (iii)).

(a) **Single drops** of sample (Expts. E1, E2, E3, E7 and E8).

(i) The paper is dipped through the buffer and blotted well between clean sheets of filter paper.

(ii) The blotted paper is picked up by one end, the midline is placed over the button-ended glass rod which is then replaced on the Vee-support. Each lower end of the paper is then carefully placed in one of the buffer compartments so that the paper hangs as an inverted, open Vee.

(iii) The sample or samples are applied at the origins (Fig. 24), using a micropipette or a melting point tube whose end has been rounded off in a flame, so that it will not damage the paper surface.

(b) **Many drops** of sample or samples to be applied *or* electrophoresis after chromatography (Expts. E4, E5 and E6).

(i) Drops of sample are applied to the origin of the *dry* paper strip with drying between each application. A dried one-way chromatogram may be used directly.

(ii) The paper is now to be wetted at both ends and a dry strip left at the centre. To do this it is held firmly at each end and dipped by inserting it about 2 cm from the origin line and drawing it through the buffer towards one end of the paper. This is repeated on the dry part of the paper on the other side of the origin. Care is taken not to wet the origin line and the paper is carefully and rapidly blotted.

(iii) The blotted paper is picked up by one end, the midline is placed over the button-ended glass rod which is then replaced on the Vee-support. Each lower end of the paper is then carefully placed in one of the buffer compartments so that the paper hangs as an inverted, open Vee.

(iv) Using a capillary tube containing buffer, wet the dry origin area so that buffer diffuses into the sample. Do not wet the sample directly.

Operation

(i) Insertion of electrophoresis assembly into the tank (Fig. 25).

    (*a*) Do not allow more time to elapse than is necessary after the paper is wetted and the sample has been applied before:—

    (*b*) picking the unit up carefully and steadily (to avoid spillage of the buffer) and lowering it into the tank.

    (*c*) Remove the polythene stoppers from the holes in the lid and put them into a safe place to avoid loss.

    (*d*) Place the lid on the tank: the electrodes will protrude through the holes in readiness for power pack connections.

(ii) Plug the electric leads into the electrodes. Ensuring correct polarities, connect to the power supply.

(iii) Turn on the current. Do not touch the apparatus again until the current is switched off.

(iv) At the end of the experiment, turn off the current, remove the leads from the electrodes, take off the lid and lift the electrophoresis assembly carefully out of the tank.

(v) Remove the paper with the aid of a second glass rod, as shown in Figs. 26*a*–26*e* and blot the ends which were immersed in the buffer by gently touching on to a clean filter paper.

(vi) Dry the paper rapidly, by hanging in an oven at 105°C, or in front of an infra-red heater. About 10 minutes is sufficient. In some cases drying in a draught of cold air is to be preferred.

(vii) Unscrew the electrode pillars and wash thoroughly. The platinised wire can be adequately washed by dipping into water up to the level of the circular groove. Shake off excess water. Do not heat the polythene.

(viii) Locate the separated substances as described for Chromatography, p. 22, using the reagent stated in each specific experiment.

TWO-WAY SEPARATIONS

As with chromatography, it would be equally desirable if one could carry out effective two-way separations. Unfortunately, although the composition and nature of the buffer can be changed,

G

the principle of electro-migration remains. The result of a two-way electrophoretic separation would be simply to spread the compounds out roughly along the diagonal of the paper as a slightly longer one-way run and little would have been accomplished.

Fortunately, it is possible to couple the two techniques of chromatography and electrophoresis, to provide two-way separations. Either technique may be used for the first one-way run and followed by the other. All that is necessary is to ensure that, after the first run, the solvent or buffer can be completely removed from the paper in readiness for the second run. To this end, volatile organic buffers are selected to replace the original inorganic salt buffers, e.g. pyridine–acetic acid replaces sodium citrate.

Paper

Use a 30×10 cm paper. Mark a single origin 2 cm up on the 15 cm mid-line.

Mechanics

(a) **Chromatography followed by electrophoresis:** The sample is applied to the origin, the paper formed into a cylinder 10 cm high and placed into the tank for ascending chromatography, using a volatile solvent. When the solvent has risen to the top of the paper, remove the paper and dry it. Apply the buffer to the paper (see pp. 83, 84) and carry out electrophoresis in the long direction of the paper. Then dry and locate the substances as described above under ' operation ' p. 85.

(b) **Electrophoresis followed by chromatography:** The sample and volatile buffer are applied, as described on pp. 83, 84, depending on the mixture being separated, and the number of drops which must be applied. Electrophoresis is carried out in the long direction of the paper, which is then removed and dried. The paper is formed into a cylinder, 10 cm tall, and run as an ascending chromatogram, dried and located as described above under ' operation '.

Solvent and Buffer

Choose one buffer and one solvent suitable for the compounds to be separated. Check that the one used first is capable of being evaporated completely off the paper by a cold draught.

EXPERIMENTS IN PAPER
ELECTROPHORESIS

BASIC

(i) All experiments should be run at about 250 V d.c. for at least one hour, or 100 V d.c. for 2–4 hours.

(ii) For all experiments, follow the directions given in section ' Practice of Paper Electrophoresis ', pp. 80–86.

Experiment E1: Separation of ink pigments and indicators

Principle: (*a*) To illustrate the technique of electrophoresis.

(*b*) To demonstrate how the components in a mixture of compounds are separated by electrophoresis.

(*c*) To demonstrate that indicators, and some of the pigments in inks are ionisable molecules.

Apparatus: See illustrations and list of parts, pp. 80, 81.

Chemicals: (*a*) Inks (see pp. 115–117)

Brown	-	-	-	*Part M200*
Royal Blue	-	-	-	*Part M201*
Black	-	-	-	*Part M204*

(*b*) Indicators

Congo Red	-	-	-	*Part M210*
Phenol Red	-	-	-	*Part M211*
Bromphenol Blue	-	-	-	*Part M212*
Indicator mixture	-	-	-	*Part M213*

Buffer: Equal volumes of—

(*a*) N/10 ammonia and N/25 ammonium acetate (3·08 g/l.).

or

(*b*) N/10 acetic acid and N/25 ammonium acetate (3·08 g/l.).

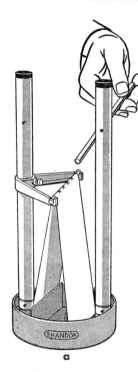

Fig. 26 (*this page and opposite*): Removal of the paper strip after electrophoresis. The current is switched off, the terminals disconnected, the lid removed, and the electrode assembly carefully lifted out of the tank. The paper is removed as follows: (a) and (b), insert a second glass rod under the paper; (c), lift the paper on two rods away from the assembly: if the two ends are very wet they can be blotted rapidly but gently, by lowering them on to a sheet of filter or blotting paper; (d), remove the rod which supported the apex, and apply a stainless steel clip, Part N, to one end of the paper (do not allow the two sides to flap together); (e), withdraw the second glass rod and hang paper vertically to dry in an oven, or in front of an infra-red heater or hot-air fan.

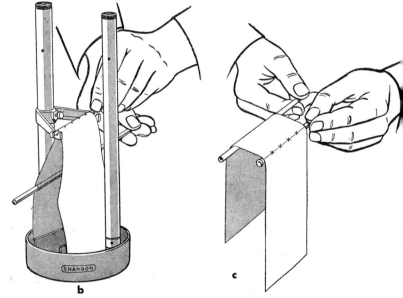

a

b

c

Procedure: (see Figs. 23–26*e*)—

(i) Mark the origins. Dip the paper in the buffer. Blot well. Place over the glass rod and insert into the Vee support of the electrophoresis assembly, with each end of the paper immersed in the solution of either compartment.

(ii) Place separately on four different origins at the apex of the paper strip, one drop of each of the indicators and their mixture; or one drop of each of three inks, and, on the fourth origin, a mixture of brown and black for comparison with Expts. C1 and E5.

(iii) Assemble the apparatus and start the current.

(iv) Observe the paper through the glass tank at frequent intervals and note the visible separation and movement of the coloured substances across the paper under the influence of the electric current.

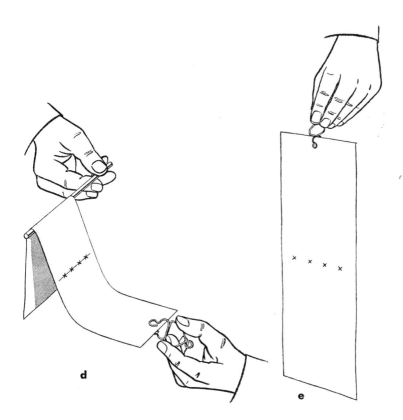

(v) Run the electrophoretogram for a suitable time, at least one hour at 250V. Switch off and disconnect the leads from the apparatus.

(vi) Remove the paper from the tank and dry it. Observe that some pigment, which is not ionised, remains at the origin.

Conclusions:

(i) Paper electrophoresis is a simple procedure for the separation of the ionisable components of a mixture.

(ii) The separation and movement of coloured compounds by paper electrophoresis can be observed visually.

(iii) Inks are made up of a mixture of ionisable and non-ionisable pigments, which travel at different rates when subjected to paper electrophoresis.

Plate 7: (facing p. 69)

Showing a separation of the component dyes of writing inks. One-way electrophoretogram of the component pigments of inks. Ammonia : ammonium acetate buffer.

Note and compare this separation with the chromatographic separations, Plates 1–3. Again the components of each ink separate in somewhat different order and manner.

Experiment E2. Separation of dyes in a mixture

Principle: (*a*) To show the characteristic invariable movement
of a compound regardless of whether it is alone
or in a mixture with other compounds which
separate well from it.
(*b*) To show that some substances travel toward the
anode, others toward the cathode.

Apparatus: See illustrations and list of parts, pp. 80, 81.

Chemicals: (see pp. 115–117)—

Fluorescein	-	-	*Part M250*
Tartrazine	-	-	*Part M251*
Malachite Green	-		*Part M252*
Mixture of Fluorescein, Tartrazine and Malachite Green			*Part M253*

Buffer: Equal volumes of—
(*a*) N/10 ammonia and N/25 ammonium acetate
(3·08 g/l.).
                              or
(*b*) N/10 acetic acid and N/25 ammonium acetate
(3·08 g/l.).

Procedure: (see Figs. 23–26*e*)—
(i) Place one drop of each of the pure dyes and one drop
of the mixture individually on four separate origins at
the apex of the paper strip.
(ii) Assemble the apparatus and start the current.
(iii) Observe the paper through the glass tank at frequent
intervals and note the visible separation and movement
of the pigments across the paper under the influence of
the electric current.
(iv) Run the electrophoretogram for a suitable time, then
switch off and disconnect the leads from the apparatus.
(v) Remove the paper from the tank and dry it.
(vi) Observe that each dye, regardless of whether it is by
itself or comes from the mixture of the dyes, moves at
the same speed and in the same direction. Malachite
green and fluorescein move in one direction, while
tartrazine moves in the opposite direction.

Conclusions:

(i) The separation and movement of coloured compounds by paper electrophoresis can be observed visually.

(ii) The direction and rate of travel of an ionisable compound is the same whether it is applied as a pure substance or comes from a mixture containing other compounds.

(iii) Some ions are positively charged and others negatively charged and, thus, move in opposite directions on paper electrophoresis.

Experiment E3. Separation of amino acids—variation of buffer pH

Principle: (a) To show that amino acids can be separated by paper electrophoresis.

(b) To demonstrate the location of colourless compounds separated by paper electrophoresis.

(c) To demonstrate that the direction of movement of amino acids is pH-dependent.

Apparatus: [See illustrations and list of parts, pp. 80, 81.

Chemicals: [(see pp. 115–117)—

DL–aspartic acid	-	-	*Part M10*
DL–leucine	-	-	-	*Part M24*
DL–lysine -	-	-	-	*Part M25*
Amino acid mixture	-	-	*Part M43*

Buffer: 10 ml pyridine + 0·8 ml glacial acetic acid made up to 250 ml with distilled water. pH = 6·1. (See Note below.)

Locating reagent:

Ninhydrin -   -   -   -   *Part M272*

Dissolve 200 mg in 100 ml acetone.

Keeps indefinitely in a refrigerator.

Procedure: (see Figs. 23–26e)—

(i) Place one drop of each of the amino acids and one drop of the mixture individually on four separate origins at the apex of the paper strip.

(ii) Assemble the apparatus and start the current.

(iii) Run the electrophoretogram for a suitable time, then switch off and disconnect the leads from the apparatus.

(iv) Remove the paper from the tank and dry as rapidly as possible.

(v) Pour the locating reagent into the dip tray (Fig. 10) and dip the electrophoretogram through the reagent.

(vi) Heat the papers in an oven at 100–105°C for 2 minutes. Note the blue or purple spots at the points reached by the three amino acids. Observe that the amino acids move at different rates and in both directions.

Conclusions:

(i) Locating reagents may be used for showing up the positions of colourless compounds on paper electrophoretic strips by transforming them into coloured spots.

(ii) The direction and rate of travel of an ionisable compound is the same whether it is applied as a pure substance or comes from a mixture containing other compounds.

(iii) Some ions are charged positively and others negatively and, thus, move in opposite directions on paper electrophoresis.

Note:

If time permits, it is instructive to repeat the experiment with each of two other buffer solutions (see Expt. E9 note (iii)):

N/10 acetic acid

N/10 ammonia

You will then be able to observe that amino acids may reverse their charge and travel to the opposite electrode when the buffer is changed from an acid to an alkaline pH. This is so because amino acids carry both acidic and basic groups, the relative ionisation of which is influenced by the pH (see p. 77).

Experiment E4. Electrophoretic separation of amino acids in fruit juices

Principle: (*a*) To demonstrate the use of paper electrophoresis in separation and identification of amino acids from natural sources.

(*b*) To show that uncharged molecules such as sugars do not separate electrophoretically.

Apparatus: See illustrations and list of parts, pp. 80, 81.

Chemicals: (see pp. 115–117)—

> *Mixture of DL–aspartic acid,*
> *DL–leucine and DL–lysine*   *Part M43*

Materials: Orange and lemon.

Buffer: 10 ml pyridine + 0·8 ml glacial acetic acid, made up to 250 ml with distilled water. pH = 6·1.

Locating reagents: (*a*) amino acids—

> *Ninhydrin -   -   -   -   Part M272*
> Dissolve 200 mg in 100 ml acetone.
> Keeps indefinitely in a refrigerator.

>   (*b*) sugars—

m-phenylene diamine - - -		0·5 g
stannous chloride - - -		1·2 g
acetic acid - - - - -		20 ml
ethanol - - - - -		80 ml

Procedure: (see Figs. 23–26*e*)—

(i) Squeeze fresh juice from an orange and a lemon, keeping each separate. Centrifuge or filter a few ml.

(ii) Dip the paper in buffer, blot and set up for electrophoresis.

(iii) Place one drop of each juice individually on two separate origins at the apex of the paper strip, and a drop of the amino acid mixture on a third origin.

(iv) Assemble the apparatus and start the current.

(v) Run the electrophoretogram for a suitable time (1–1½ hours). Switch off and disconnect the leads from the apparatus.

(vi) Remove the paper from the tank and dry as rapidly as possible.

   (vii) Pour the ninhydrin reagent into the dip tray (Fig. 10) and dip the chromatogram through the reagent.

(viii) Heat the paper for two minutes at 100–105°C in the oven.

   (ix) Observe that several coloured spots are obtained for each of the juices and the amino acid mixture.

   (x) Mark the positions of the amino acids with pencil. Compare the electrophoretograms of the juices with the chromatograms obtained in Chromatography Expt. C9 and observe that fewer spots are obtained by electrophoresis.

   (xi) Now treat the electrophoretogram with the sugar locating reagent and heat for up to five minutes at 105°C. Note that no separation of sugars has occurred, although Chromatography Expt. C11 shows that a mixture of sugars is present.

Conclusion:

   (i) Amino acids from natural substances may be separated by electrophoresis, but the resolution is not as good as that obtained by chromatography.

   (ii) Neutral sugars are not ionised and so remain unseparated as a single spot near the origin. Electrophoresis is not a suitable technique for the separation of non-ionised molecules.

Notes:

(i) The reason for this less satisfactory resolution is that, on electrophoresis, the amino acids tend to move in groups, instead of individually; the neutral amino acids, e.g. leucine, stay fairly close to the origin. There is often some separation of the basic and the acidic amino acids but rarely of the neutral amino acids.

(ii) The salts present in biological solutions do not present the problem which occurs in chromatography—see Chromatography Expts. C14 and C15—and desalting is not therefore usually necessary.

SUPPLEMENTARY
Experiments in Paper Electrophoresis

Experiment E5.   Chromatography-Electrophoresis—two-way separation of an ink mixture

Principle: To demonstrate two-way separations by means of chromatography followed by electrophoresis.

Apparatus: See illustrations and list of parts, pp. 80, 81.

Chemicals: (see pp. 115–117)—

Brown ink	-	-	-	*Part M200*
Blue ink	-	-	-	*Part M201*
Black ink	-	-	-	*Part M204*

Solvent: n-butanol : ethanol : 2N ammonia
(60 : 20 : 20 by volume).

Buffer: Equal volumes of—
N/10 ammonia and N/25 ammonium acetate (3·08 g/l)

Procedure: (see Figs. 23, 8, 24–26e)—

(i) Mark a single origin, 2 cm from the side of the paper. Apply one single drop of black or blue ink and dry with cold air. Then apply, on the same origin, one drop of brown ink and dry again.

(ii) Using the tongued clips, Part G, form the paper into a cylinder 10 cm high and run in the butanol : ethanol solvent for 1–2 hours, or until the solvent front reaches the top of the paper. Remove and thoroughly dry the chromatogram. The paper can be kept at this stage until the next laboratory period.

(iii) Carefully dip the paper in buffer as described for two-way separations, pp. 85, 86, and continue as described in Expt. E1. Run for $1\frac{1}{2}$ to 3 hours, depending upon the voltage.

Conclusion:

Two-way separations, using chromatography followed by electrophoresis, show increased resolution of substances compared to one-way separation, using either technique alone.

Notes:

(i) Two-way separations obtained by this procedure are different from those obtained by two-way chromatography.

(ii) For such a two-way separation to be effective, the solvent or buffer used for the first separation must be completely volatile. Thus, after drying, a paper free from residual solvent is ready for the second separation.

Plate 8: (facing p. 69)

Showing a separation of the component dyes of inks by chromatography-electrophoresis. Two-way separations of the pigments present in a mixture of brown and black, and brown and blue inks. The first separation was by chromatography with the butanol : ethanol : ammonia solvent in the 10 cm direction and the second separation was by electrophoresis with ammonia : ammonium acetate buffer in the 30 cm direction. Some of these spots are diffuse for the reasons given under Plate 4. Compare them with the compact spots of amino acids shown in Plate 9.

Experiment E6. Electrophoresis-Chromatography—two-way separation of amino acids.

Principle: To demonstrate two-way separation of amino acids by electrophoresis followed by chromatography.

Apparatus: See illustrations and list of parts, pp. 80, 81.

Chemicals: One of the fruit juices prepared for Expt. E4.

Locating reagent: amino acids—

> *Ninhydrin* - - - - *Part M272*
> Dissolve 200 mg in 100 ml acetone.
> Keeps indefinitely in a refrigerator.

Buffer: 10 ml pyridine $+$ 0·8 ml glacial acetic acid made up to 250 ml with distilled water. pH $=$ 6·1.

Solvents: (*a*) ethanol : water : ammonia soln. 0·880
  (80 : 10 : 10 by volume) or

  (*b*) *n*-butanol : acetic acid : water
  (60 : 15 : 25 by volume).

Procedure: (see Figs. 23–26*e* and Fig. 8)—

(i) Mark a single origin 2 cm from the side of the paper on the 15 cm mid-line. Apply a few drops of juice with intermittent drying of the spots.

(ii) Carefully wet the paper with the buffer: run for 1–1½ hours (at 250V).

(iii) Turn off the current, remove and dry the paper rapidly with cold air in a fume cupboard.

(iv) Using the tongued clips, Part G, form the paper into a cylinder 10 cm high and run the chromatogram in either of the solvents until the solvent reaches the top of the paper (about 1 hour).

(v) Remove and dry the chromatogram and treat with ninhydrin reagent in the dip tray, Fig. 10.

Conclusion:

Two-way separation using electrophoresis followed by chromatography shows increased resolution over either technique alone.

Notes:

(i) Two-way separations obtained by this procedure are different from those obtained by two-way chromatography.

(ii) For such a two-way separation to be effective, the solvent or buffer used for the first separation must be completely volatile. Thus, after drying, a paper free from residual solvent is ready for the second separation.

Plate 9: (facing p. 69)

Showing a separation of amino acids by electrophoresis-chromatography. Two-way separation of the amino acids present in fresh orange juice. The first separation was by electrophoresis in the pyridine : acetic acid buffer and the second separation was by chromatography in butanol : acetic acid : water solvent.

In mixtures of biological origin, i.e. mixtures which contain salt, it is usual to run the electrophoresis first. This removes the inorganic ions from the areas occupied by the amino acids and prevents their interference with the subsequent chromatography. Note how compact these spots are.

Experiment E7.   Electrophoresis—separation of serum proteins

Principle: To demonstrate the separation of large colloidal molecules, such as proteins.

Apparatus: See illustrations and list of parts, pp. 80, 81.

Materials: Human blood or serum.

Buffer: *Sodium barbitone* -   -   -   5 g

Sodium acetate -   -   -   -   3·24 g

Hydrochloric acid N/10 -   -   32·2 ml

Dissolve the sodium salts in 940 ml water, add the acid, adjust the pH to 8·6 with a little more acid if necessary, and make up to 1 litre.

Stains: 0·25 per cent Light Green   } in 3 per cent trichloro-
                        or   acetic acid in water.
           0·1 per cent Azocarmine B   } Filter.

Preparation of serum:

Obtain samples of about 0·5 ml of human blood from different subjects and allow to clot by standing for one-half hour at room temperature. Centrifuge and pipette off the supernatant serum. Serum can be stored in the refrigerator for some days and can be prepared in advance for this experiment.

Sera, including abnormal samples, can usually be obtained by prior arrangement from a local hospital; 0·2 ml is adequate.

Procedure: (see Figs. 23–26e)—

(i) Cut the 30 × 10 cm sheet to form two pieces, each 30 × 5 cm (see Note (i)).

(ii) Draw a line along the 15 cm mid-line. On this mark two origin lines, each 2 cm wide, and each 0·25 cm from opposite edges of the paper. This leaves 0·5 cm central gap.

(iii) Dip paper in the buffer, blot well and place in position over the glass rod on the Vee support of the electrophoresis assembly.

(iv) Apply about 8 µl. of serum from a micropipette or melting point tube as a streak along one 2 cm line and a similar volume of another serum to the other 2 cm line.

(v) Assemble the apparatus. Switch on and run for 5 hours.

H

(vi) Turn off the current, remove the paper, blot the ends, and dry at 105°C for about 10 minutes. The drying stage is usual in electrophoresis but can be omitted without detriment here, and the wet strip stained directly.

(vii) Immerse the strip in the stain, except for 5 cm length from each end and stand for 15 minutes (see Note (vii)).

(viii) Transfer the strip to 5 per cent acetic acid in tap water and rinse out background stain by rocking occasionally for 5 minutes.

(ix) Change rinse solution and repeat for a further 5 minutes, or until the background colour disappears, leaving the paper white again.

(x) Rinse in methanol and dry in air. Observe the bands (see Note (ii)).

Conclusion:

Paper electrophoresis is a simple procedure, useful for the separation of proteins.

Notes:

(i) Only a 5 cm wide strip should be used for this experiment when the UNIKIT power pack is supplying current. When a larger power pack is used, the usual 10 cm wide strip can be used. This is because the conductivity of the buffer is very high compared to the buffers used in the other experiments and it might overload the UNIKIT power pack, especially in hot climates.

(ii) Four main bands will be observed after staining, together with a weak band, which is not always visible. To observe the weak band (α_1 globulin) an optimum amount of serum must be used; too little serum will not contain enough to yield a visible stain, and with too much serum the α_1 is obscured by the very heavy albumin band.

(iii) In this experiment, the origin is a narrow 2 cm band or streak, and not a circular spot. This enables minor components to be seen more easily. (See pp. 83, 84, ' Application of Sample '.)

(iv) Experiments such as this are carried out routinely in hospital laboratories to determine serum protein levels. Increase or decrease in the concentration of the various proteins is of diagnostic significance (see Ref. 2, Book List).

(v) The conditions described here are adjusted to suit the UNIKIT power pack and are not those used in hospital laboratories. Normally, the buffer is used at double the concentration described here, the potential drop is 2 to 2·5 volts/cm, and the time of run is 16–20 hours.

Increased salt concentration produces sharper bands but requires longer time for equal length of separation. Samples can, however, be accumulated during the day and all set going for an overnight run.

(vi) It is obvious from the above that conditions are flexible and can often be adjusted to suit individual convenience.

(vii) Skin is a protein and therefore the fingers will be dyed if they contact the stain solutions. Forceps, or polythene gloves, should therefore be used when staining and rinsing the strips.

(viii) The stain can be used a number of times.

Experiment E8.   Electrophoresis—determination of the iso-electric point of a protein

Principle: (a) To demonstrate that proteins can exist as cations, as neutral molecules, or as anions, depending on the pH of the solution.

(b) To show that a protein will not migrate at its iso-electric point.

Apparatus: See illustrations and list of parts, pp. 80, 81.

Chemicals:

Albumin, bovine serum	-	-	0·2 g		
Glucose	-	-	-	-	-	0·1 g
Water	-	-	-	-	-	10 ml

Cover albumin with water; stand some hours; very gently shake to dissolve: add glucose. Prepare in advance of the experiment.

Note: This experiment can be more simply performed if Armour's bovine serum albumin sterile 30% solution is available, when a dilution of one part in 15 of the solution may be used in place of the solid albumin i.e. 10 ml of the dilution + 0·1 g glucose.

Buffers: Citric acid/sodium citrate—to prepare a series of buffers of different pH's (see Note (ii) below), mix solutions as shown in the table below:—

Solution A = citric acid . H_2O - 8·40 g/l. (=M/25)

Solution B = *tri*-sodium citrate

. $2H_2O$ - - - - - 11·76 g/l. (=M/25)

pH	Soln. A	Soln. B
	(ml)	(ml)
3·6	14·9	5·1
4·2	12·3	7·7
4·4	11·4	8·6
4·6	10·3	9·7
4·8	9·2	10·8
5·0	8·2	11·8
5·6	5·5	14·5
6·6	1·4	18·6

Stains: For protein:—

0·25 per cent *Light Green*
or
0·1 per cent *Azocarmine B*
} in 3 per cent trichloro-
acetic acid in water.

Locating reagent: for glucose:—

m-phenylene diamine	-	-	-	0·5 g
stannous chloride	-	-	-	1·2 g
acetic acid -	-	-	-	20 ml
ethanol	-	-	-	80 ml

Procedure: (see Figs. 23–26e)—

(a) *As a class experiment* where a number of UNIKITS are available each student should prepare 150 ml of a different buffer and use this for the experiment.

(i) Cut the 30 × 10 cm sheet to form two pieces 30 × 5 cm.

(ii) Draw a line along the origin position of one piece, dip in the buffer, blot well, and place in position over the glass rod of the Vee support.

(iii) Apply the albumin solution as a streak on the origin line omitting a few mm at each side of the strip. Assemble the apparatus and run for at least two hours, although 4–5 hours would be preferable.

(iv) Turn off the current, remove the paper, blot the ends and dry at 105°C for about 10 minutes.

(v) Cut the paper into two strips 30 × 2·5 cm. Stain one for protein and the other for glucose as follows.

(vi) For protein; cover the strip, except for 5 cm from each end, with the light green or azocarmine solution for 15 minutes. Transfer the strip to 5 per cent acetic acid in tap water and rinse out background stain by rocking occasionally for 5 minutes. Blot and dry the strip.

(vii) For glucose; dip the second strip in the sugar reagent and heat for up to 5 minutes at 100–105°C. Glucose will appear as a brown spot on a light yellow background.

(b) *As a single experiment* the run can be confined to one apparatus with the following modification to the above procedure.

(i) Draw a line along the origin position and then cut the 30×10 cm paper into ten, 30×1 cm strips. Take eight strips and mark one for each different buffer pH, p. 104.

(ii) Use the pH 4·8 buffer for the electrode compartments.

(iii) Dip one strip through each of the different buffers, blot all and hang carefully over the Vee support.

(iv) Apply a few microlitres of albumin solution to each strip in as narrow a line as possible.

(v) Assemble the apparatus and run for a minimum of 2 hours, although 4–5 hours would be preferable.

(vi) Turn off the current, remove and dry the strips at 105°C for about 10 minutes. Cut each strip into two pieces each $30 \times 0·5$ cm.

(vii) Stain one strip of each pair for protein as in (a) (vi) above. When quite dry, mark carefully the position of the albumin band.

(viii) Now treat the other strip of each pair with the sugar reagent as in (a) (vii) above and, very carefully, mark the position of the glucose.

(ix) Note the relative positions of the albumin and the glucose.

Conclusions:

(i) At pH 3·6 the albumin has travelled rapidly towards the cathode showing that it is moving as a cation. It has separated from glucose.

(ii) At pH 6·6 the albumin has moved towards the anode showing that it is now moving as an anion. It has again separated from the glucose.

(iii) At pH around 4·6 to 4·8 the albumin and glucose spots are coincident showing that the albumin is not moving in the electric field and is therefore acting as a neutral molecule. The actual position of this spot has moved slightly from the origin and this is a measure of the electro-osmotic flow. The amount of movement will depend on the length of time for which the experiment was run.

(iv) The fact that a substance is located on the origin position at the end of the experiment does not then prove that it has not moved. It may be that its rate of migration exactly balances the electro-osmotic flow in the reverse direction.

Notes:

(i) By means of this procedure it is possible to determine the iso-electric point of any protein. In order to do this for an unknown protein, a preliminary experiment is run using buffers differing by one pH unit on each different strip; this will indicate the approximate region of the iso-electric point. The experiment is repeated with buffers differing by 0·2 or even 0·1 units of pH.

(ii) When preparing a set of buffers for determination of the accurate iso-electric point, choose stock solutions which will cover the whole range, e.g. as above the citric acid–sodium citrate covers the whole pH range of this experiment. The reason for this is that the particular buffer salt can affect the actual figure of the result in particular cases. Hence, changing from citrate to phosphate buffer may show an apparent discrepancy if this is not borne in mind.

(iii) It was stated on p. 78 that, in order to measure the electro-osmotic flow, a substance of similar size to the ionised substance is used. In this experiment, however, we have departed from this procedure and used a small neutral molecule to study a large protein. The reason for this is that glucose is readily available, whereas the standard neutral molecules of large size may be difficult to obtain for many schools and colleges. Nevertheless the principle is equally well demonstrated here.

Experiment E9: Electrophoresis—separation of cations, the metals of Group 3B (Zn, Co, Mn, Ni)

Principle: To show that inorganic cations can be separated by paper electrophoresis.

Apparatus: See illustrations and list of parts, pp. 80, 81.

Chemicals: (see pp. 115–117)—

Zinc nitrate - - -	*Part M220*	
Cobalt nitrate - - -	*Part M221*	
Manganese nitrate - -	*Part M222*	
Nickel nitrate - - -	*Part M223*	
Mixture of four nitrates -	*Part M224*	

Locating reagent: metals—

Sodium pentacyanoammine-ferroate - - - -	*Part M270*
Rubeanic acid - - -	*Part M271*

(Preparation see Appendix)

Buffer: 1·5 per cent citric acid in water.

Procedure: (see Figs. 23–26*e*)—

(i) Place one drop of each of the metal nitrates and one drop of the mixture individually on five different origins at the apex of the 30 × 10 cm strip.

(ii) Assemble the apparatus and start the current.

(iii) Prepare the locating reagent as described in the Appendix.

(iv) Run for approximately 1·3 hours. Switch off and disconnect the leads.

(v) Remove the paper, dry as rapidly as possible, and fume with ammonia to neutralise the citric acid.

(vi) Dip the strip in the locating reagent and rinse in 2 per cent acetic acid until the background is white. Remove and blot the paper.

(vii) Mark the positions of the individual cations and note that the relative rates of migration are the same for each ion whether in pure solution or in a mixture.

Conclusion:

Inorganic ions can be separated by paper electrophoresis.

Notes:

(i) The separation of cobalt and zinc is not complete on every occasion, but the presence of one or both is seen from the different colours produced by the locating reagent.

(ii) If the experiment is allowed to run too long, then the manganese runs off the paper into the buffer.

(iii) Citric acid solution is not a buffer, but solutions of acids and bases are often used in electrophoresis. These are loosely referred to as 'buffers' as they replace the buffers otherwise used.

(iv) Comparatively little work has been carried out on the electrophoresis of inorganic cations mainly because excellent chromatographic methods were available before the advent of electrophoresis.

Plate 5: (facing p. 68)

Showing a separation of the cations of zinc, cobalt, manganese and nickel (group 3B). Two ascending separations, one descending separation and one electrophoretic separation. The chromatographic solvent was acetone : water : HCl in both cases and the electrophoretic buffer was 1·5 per cent citric acid.

The three types of separation are shown side-by-side for comparison. Note that the ascending and descending runs are very similar, but not identical, whereas the electrophoretic separation is quite different, as would be expected from a technique using an entirely different principle. Observe the variable green line in the ascending separations (see Note (i) Expt. C6).

BOOK LIST

Introductory reading:
1. *Elements of Chromatography*, by T. I. Williams.
   Blackie & Son Ltd., London, 1954.

Standard works:
2. *Chromatographic and Electrophoretic Techniques*, edited by Ivor Smith.
   Wm. Heinemann Medical Books Ltd., London, and Interscience Publishers, Inc., New York, 1962.
3. *Paper Chromatography and Paper Electrophoresis*, by R. J. Block, E. L. Durrum and G. Zweig.
   Academic Press, New York, 1958.
4. *Papierchromatographie*, by F. Cramer. (English and German.) Verlag Chemie, G.m.b.H., Weinheim.
5. *Chromatography*, by D. Waldi (English and German).
   E. Merck, Darmstadt.
6. *Chromatographic Methods of Inorganic Analysis*, by F. H. Pollard and J. F. W. McOmie.
   Butterworths, London.
7. *Principles and Applications of Paper Electrophoresis*, by Ch. Wunderly.
   Elsevier Publishing Co., Amsterdam, 1961.
8. *Chromatography*, by E. Heftmann.
   Reinhold Publishing Corporation, New York, 1961.

FILM

Principles of Chromatography. Twenty-minute instructional film, 16 mm, sound and colour, by Ivor Smith and John B. Jepson, available from:—
(a) Educational Foundation for Visual Aids,
    33 Queen Anne Street, London, W.1.
(b) McGraw-Hill, U.S.A.
(c) Via the Cultural Attachés, British Embassies of various countries.

THE SHANDON 'UNIKIT'

SPECIFICATIONS

AND

ILLUSTRATIONS

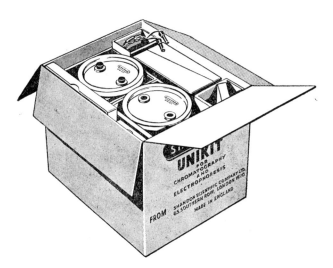

Fig. 27: The UNIKIT in its shipping carton.

THE SHANDON UNIKIT*

For studying and teaching the principles of
Paper Chromatography and Electrophoresis

2250 SHANDON UNIKIT:
In fitted shipping carton, $16\frac{1}{2} \times 14 \times 14$ in. ($42 \times 33 \times 33$ cm). Gross weight 17 lb (7·8 kg); net weight 12 lb (5·5 kg). Comprising Manual 2251 and Parts A–N below.

2251 Teaching Level Manual for Chromatography and Electrophoresis on Paper (*Shandon Scientific Education Manual No.* 1) (130 pp. and 9 colour plates), by J. G. Feinberg, B.Sc., M.Sc., D.V.M., M.Inst.Biol., and Ivor Smith, B.Sc., Ph.D., F.R.I.C., M.Inst.Biol.

Part A: 2 ✕ **UNIKIT Tanks, 2255,** heavy borosilicate glass, 280×135 mm approx., with gallery 150 mm diam., having ground rim.

Part B: 2 ✕ **Lids, 2256,** moulded polythene, about 170 mm diam., with annular groove to engage tank rim. Two holes allow emergence of electrode terminals and require lid removal (and, therefore, current disconnection for safety purposes) at end of electrophoresis experiments; holes to be closed by polythene stoppers during chromatography. Twelve polythene stoppers supplied.

Part C: 1 ✕ **Solvent Trough, 2282,** moulded polythene, about 150 mm long, nominal capacity 50 ml, with integral grooved channels to accommodate two glass anti-syphon rods (included in Part D). For use in descending chromatography.

*World Patents pending. Regd. Design Nos. 902603, 90260A, 902606, 904257. DBGM 39515.

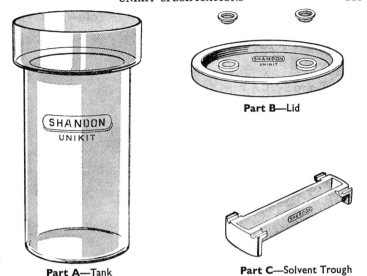

Part B—Lid

Part A—Tank

Part C—Solvent Trough

Part D: 1 set   Glass Rods, 2258, for use with solvent trough in descending chromatography, comprising:—
2 × anti-syphon rods, 140 × 5 mm;
1 × anchor rod, with upturned end, 135 × 6 mm.

Part E: 1 pkt   Filter Paper, 2265, Whatman No. 1, 100 sheets, 30 × 10 cm, for use in descending chromatography and in electrophoresis.

Part F: 1 pkt   Filter Paper, 2266, Whatman No. 1, 100 sheets, 25 × 25 cm, for use in ascending chromatography.

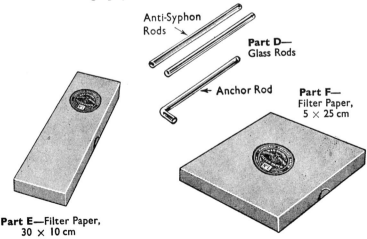

Anti-Syphon Rods

Part D—
Glass Rods

Anchor Rod

Part F—
Filter Paper,
5 × 25 cm

Part E—Filter Paper,
30 × 10 cm

Part G: 12 X Tongued Clips, 2261, moulded plastics, 20 × 15 mm, with tongues for use in securing edges of 25 cm square paper to form a cylinder in ascending chromatography.

Part H: 1 X Electrophoresis Assembly, 2260, moulded polythene dish, about 120 mm diam., with two integral partitions to form two buffer compartments; integral threaded bosses engaged by two polythene hollow pillars, about 265 mm long; fitted shock-proof sockets for electrical connection, and platinised nickel-iron electrodes; moulded polythene Vee-support, with clamping screw and grooved channels for glass rod, Part J.

Part J: 1 X Glass Rod, 2260/a, with button ends, for use as paper support in electrophoresis with Part H. Dimensions 125 × 5 mm.

Park K: 1 pair Leads, Electrical, 2260/b, length 1·80 m, red and black, fitted shock-proof plugs one end, to engage electrophoresis pillar sockets. Other ends to be fitted by user with terminals appropriate to power supply.

Part G—Tongued Clips

Parts H and J—Electrophoresis
Assembly and Glass Rod

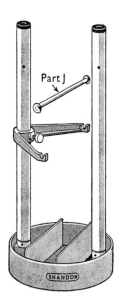

Part J

Part K—Leads, Electrical

Part L: 1 X   **Dip Tray, 2180,** moulded polythene, about 275 × 75 mm, modern stable design, with beaded edge to remove surplus reagent as paper is drawn over it, thus shortening drying time. Minimal capacity needing only about 20 ml reagent.

Part L—Dip Tray

Part M: 1 set   **UNIKIT Chemicals and Reagents, 2262,** comprising thirty-five × 5 ml vials, enumerated below; 7 spare empty vials; micro-pipette 10µl. × 2·5 µl.; Pt–Ir wire loop, 4 mm diam., mounted on glass rod. All in foamed-polystyrene ' desk '-type pack, designed for easy accessibility. In carton 30 × 23 × 9·5 cm.

Part M—
Chemicals
and Reagents

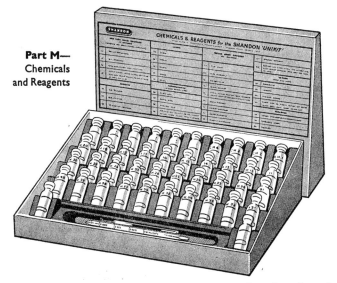

(continued overleaf)

Part M (*continued*)

Amino acids:
Concentration 0·01M in 10 per cent *iso*-propanol/water.

M10   DL–aspartic acid
M24   DL–leucine
M25   DL–lysine
M43   Amino acid marker mixture of M10, M24 and M25.

Sugars:
Dissolved in 10 per cent *iso*-propanol/water.

M72   D(+)–glucose (anhydrous) 0·5 per cent
M75   D(+)–xylose   -   - 0·5 per cent
M78   Lactose   -   -   - 0·7 per cent

Inks:
M200   Brown
M201   Royal blue
M202   Scarlet
M203   Green
M204   Black.

Indicators:
Concentration 0·05 per cent in ethanol (plus a little sodium hydroxide, when necessary, to aid solution).

M210   Congo red
M211   Phenol red
M212   Bromphenol blue
M213   Indicator mixture of M210, M211 and M212.

Metal salts solutions:
Concentration 0·3 per cent in water (with added HCl where necessary to prevent hydrolysis).

M220   Zinc nitrate
M221   Cobalt nitrate
M222   Manganese nitrate
M223   Nickel nitrate
M224   Zn–Co–Mn–Ni/nitrates
M225   Lead nitrate

Part M (*continued*)

       M226   *Copper nitrate*

       M227   *Cadmium nitrate*

       M228   *Bismuth nitrate*

       M229   *Mercuric nitrate*

       M230   *Pb–Cu–Cd–Bi–Hg̈/nitrates.*

Dyes:

Concentration 0·1 per cent in water.

       M250   *Fluorescein*

       M251   *Tartrazine*

       M252   *Malachite green*

       M253   *Dye mixture of M250, M251 and M252.*

Reagents:

Solids.

       M270   *Sodium pentacyanoammineferroate*

       M271   *Rubeanic acid*

       M272   *Ninhydrin*

       M273   *Light green*

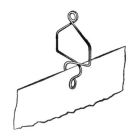

Part N—Stainless Steel Clips

Part N: pkt. 12 Stainless Steel Clips, 2118, for use in suspending chromatograms and electrophoretograms during drying.

J

2252   **Shandon UNIKIT Power Supply** (see p. 79), for use in running one to four UNIKIT electro-phoresis experiments simultaneously from one power supply.

Enamelled metal case, $15 \times 12 \cdot 5 \times 10$ cm high, containing double-wound transformer, metal rectifier, smoothing condenser, current-limiting resistors, pilot light and switch.

Input tapped for operation from 100–125V, 200–250V, 50/60 c/s a.c. mains, with $1 \cdot 8$ m three-core mains connection cable.

Output, four pairs of output sockets colour coded red and black, each having an open-circuit voltage of 350 and a short-circuit current of 10 mA through 35,000 ohm inbuilt protective resistors.

UNIKIT Power Supply

APPENDIX

All the solvents, buffers, locating reagents and stains to which reference is made in the experiments described in this Manual are collected together on pp. 120–123, for convenience in reference. Where a Part Number appears against the name, the material is included in the UNIKIT set of reagents and chemicals, Part M. Where no Part Number appears it is expected that the material will be available either in the laboratory stock or from local sources.

The instructor may decide whether students shall make up the solvents, buffers, etc., as needed, or whether a laboratory technician shall prepare in advance bulk stocks of those which are stable and do not need to be freshly made.

Table 1. Solvents

Nature of Sample	Solvent and Composition by Volume	Reference
Inks and Indicators	n-butanol ....60 ethanol ....20 ammonia 2N 20	Expts.: **C1, C2, C3, C5, C12, E5**
	water ....75 saturated aqueous ammonium sulphate 10 ethanol 15	Expts.: **C1, C2, C3, C5**
Metal Ions	acetone ....87 water.......................... 5 conc. HCl...................... 8	Expt.: **C6**
	ethanol ....90 water.............................. 5 conc. HCl...................... 5	Expt.: **C13**
	n-butanol saturated with N HC1	Expt.: **C13**
	Preparation. Add 50 ml of each liquid to a separating funnel, shake well and allow to separate. Draw off the lower layer and discard it ; use the upper layer as the chromatographic solvent. If droplets of water remain in the upper layer, remove them by filtration.	
Amino Acids	ethanol ....80 water............................10 ammonia soln. 0·880 ...10	Expts.: **C8, C9, C10, C14, C15, E6**
	n-butanol ....60 acetic acid....................15 water 25	Expts.: **C10, C14, E6**
Sugars	ethyl acetate ....55 pyridine.........................25 water 20	Expt.: **C11**
Plant (plastid) pigments	acetone ....10 petroleum ether (40–60°C) 90	Expt.: **C7**
	chloroform ....30 petroleum ether (40–60°C) 70	Expt.: **C7**

Table 2. Buffers

Nature of Sample	Buffer Composition	Reference
Inks and Indicators	ammonia soln. N/10 ....50 ammonium acetate N/25 (3·08 g/l.) 50	Expts.: **E1, E2, E5**
	acetic acid N/10...........50 ammonium acetate N/25 (3·08 g/l.) ....••••....50	Expts.: **E1, E2**
Amino Acids	pyridine ....10ml acetic acid, glacial 0·8 ml water, distilled, to 250 ml pH = 6·1	Expts.: **E3, E4, E6**
	acetic acid N/10	Expt.: **E3**
	ammonia soln. N/10	Expt.: **E3**

Barbitone Buffer

	sodium barbitone ....5 g sodium acetate....3·24 g hydrochloric acid N/10 ....32·2 ml	Expt.: **E7**

Dissolve the sodium salts in 940 ml water, add the acid, adjust the pH to 8·6 with a little more acid if necessary, and make up to 1 litre.

Citrate Buffers
citric acid/sodium citrate. To prepare a series of buffers of
   different pH's mix solutions as shown in the table below :
Solution A = citric acid. H_2O.................8·40 g/l (= M/25)
Solution B = *tri*-sodium citrate. $2H_2O$.......11·76 g/l (= M/25)

Serum Proteins

pH	Soln. A ml	Soln. B ml	
3·6	14·9	5·1	
4·2	12·3	7·7	
4·4	11·4	8·6	
4·6	10·3	9·7	Expt.: **E8**
4·8	9·2	10·8	
5·0	8·2	11·8	
5·6	5·5	14·5	
6·6	1·4	18·6	

Metal Ions	citric acid. H_2O.......1·5 g water, distilled, to 100 ml	Expt.: **E9**

Table 3. Locating Reagents

Nature of Sample	Reagent Composition	Reference
Metal Ions Group 3B	*Solution A* sodium pentacyanoammineferroate Part M270 ....50 mg ⎫ water distilled ....20 ml ⎬ Dissolve *Solution B* rubeanic acid Part M271 ....10 mg ⎫ Make ethanol ....10 ml ⎬ saturated solution. Mix 20 ml solution A with 1·5 ml solution B. Shake a few minutes. If not then a dark purple add more B and shake. Filter. Reagent is unstable. Must be made fresh daily and stored in cold.	Expts.: **C6, C6a, C13, E9**
Pb Bi	H_2S-saturated water made alkaline with a few drops of ammonia soln. 0·880. Must be freshly prepared.	Expt.: **C13**
Amino Acids	ninhydrin Part M272 200 mg acetone ....100 ml Keeps indefinitely in a refrigerator	Expts.: **C8, C9, C10, C14, C15, E3, E4, E6**
Sugars	*m*-phenylene diamine 0·5 g stannous chloride ....1·2 g acetic acid ....20 ml ethanol ....80 ml	Expts.: **C9, C11, E4, E8**

Table 4. Protein Sample and Stains

Nature of Sample	Composition	Reference
Protein Specimen	Albumin, bovine serum .... 0·2 g glucose .... 0·1 g water distilled .... 10 ml Cover albumin with water; stand some hours; very gently shake to dissolve; add glucose.	Expt.: **E8**
Stains for Protein	light green Part M273 .... 0·25 g trichloroacetic acid .... 3 g water distilled to .... 100 ml **or** azocarmine B .... 0·1 g trichloroacetic acid .... 3 g water distilled to ....100 ml	Expts.: **E7, E8**

Miscellaneous:

Expt. C9, Note (iv) - *iso*-propanol.
Expt. C15 - - - ZeoKarb 225 resin or Dowex 50.
Expt. E7   -   -   - blood serum.
Expt. E7   -   -   - methanol.
Expt. E8   -   -   - Armour bovine serum albumin, 30 per cent sterile solution (optional).
Expt. C14 -   -   - physiological saline (0·9 per cent sodium chloride).

INDEX